COLOR IN THE SKY

FLOWERING TREES

IN OUR LANDSCAPE

By EDWIN A. MENNINGER, D.Sc.
The Flowering Tree Man

With a Foreword by
GEORGE H. M. LAWRENCE, Ph. D.
Former Head of
Bailey Hortorium, Cornell University, Ithaca, N. Y.
Hunt Botanical Library, Carnegie-Mellon University, Pittsburgh, Pa.
Fairchild Tropical Garden, Miami, Fla.

Published 1975 by
HORTICULTURAL BOOKS, Inc.
Stuart, Florida 33494

ISBN 0-9600046-3-7

To My Wife
PATSY UNDERHILL MENNINGER
who for nearly fifty years has inspired
my search for beauty among
the trees,
This Book is Affectionately Dedicated
by the Author

TABLE OF CONTENTS

ACKNOWLEDGEMENTS

My peregrinations through the forests of the world have mostly followed the arm chair route, and I have been separated only by a postage stamp from thousands of plantsmen all over the world. These contacts have been inspiring to me, stimulating my interest in the trees of other countries, enriching my acquaintance with tree flowers of a thousand kinds, encouraging me to get seeds and try to grow all of them, spurring my interest in descriptive floras of many lands, forcing me to study endlessly under a bed lamp to learn about the beautiful trees in a hundred lands I would never visit in person.

My acquaintance with plantsmen all over the world has been enriched by helpful letters from a lot of great men in the plant world who took time out of their busy schedules to tell me about flowering trees. I think of Dr. R. E. Holttum at Singapore Botanic Garden, Noel Lothian at the Adelaide Botanic Garden, Harry Oakman at the Canberra parks department, A. W. Jessep whose trail I followed from Johannesburg to Perth to Sydney and back to Perth, and a dozen other outstanding plant authorities in Australia. I have treasured many years of contacts with Victor Davies and Douglas Elliott in New Zealand, with Harry Blossfeld, Dr. Adolpho Ducke, Dr. Wilson Hoehne and others in Brazil, with Dr. Georg Leon in Peru, Dr. Julian A. Steyermark and Dr. Leon Croizat in Venezuela, and so on and on far into the night; literally hundreds of scholars have dropped their work to help me, just a plain dirt gardener by the side of the road. In my book on *Flowering Trees of the World* I listed these men and hundreds more who, like myself, were interested enough in floral beauty to help tell the world about it.

I got wonderful help from scholars in India, in tropical and south Africa, in the West Indies, in Hawaii and throughout Malaysia. It is a big world.

Right here in Florida I was stimulated by a warm friendship with Dr. David Fairchild and his wife Marian Bell Fairchild (daughter of Alexander Graham Bell). In my garden grows a beautiful *Colvillea racemosa* tree that Dr. Fairchild grew in his slathouse and gave to me. It was at a luncheon in the Fairchild home that I met the illustrious E. J. H. Corner of the Cambridge University faculty with whom I spent many happy hours looking at trees, and whose friendship I have nourished through the succeeding years. I spent much time with Dr. John Gifford of the forestry faculty of the University of Miami and enjoyed many hours riding around looking at special trees. I spent much time with Gardner Wilson in his Fantastic Gardens in South Miami, I valued a long friendship with S. John Lynch, long with the University of Miami and more recently in the nursery business at Bradenton. I learned a great deal from Dr. Julia Morton, wide awake student of tropical plants, who has continued to help me with photographs of plants, botanical guidance and suggestions about my books. Other valued Miami friends were Adolph Jordahn, first superintendent of the Fairchild Tropical Garden; H. F. Loomis of the U. S. Plant Introduction Garden, Nixon Smiley, Lucita H. Wait and many more. I am indebted to Hugh Bruce and Tinsley Halter of Palm Beach, to Carl Cowgill and Jack Holmes of Tampa, to Morgan Evans, landscaper of Disneyland and the Disney World, and to literally thousands of other people who sacrificed their own interests and time, to keep me going straight and steady in my search for the most beautiful flowering trees in the world. I often think of happy and enriching hours spent with Robert Halgrim of the Edison estate at Fort Myers, with Paul Swedroe and D. J. McSwiney at Ft. Lauderdale, with Dr. David Fairburn at Vero Beach, Robert J. Godbey of Kendall, Dr. Samuel Ayres, Jr., and Ralph Cornell in Los Angeles, Eric Golby at Bradenton, and so many more that have helped me along the way. I cannot omit Dr. Wilson Popenoe, the great plant explorer who introduced the avocado to the United States. Wilson and I were boys together in Topeka, Kansas a lifetime ago: he is my oldest plant friend and helper and I owe him much. Not the least of my friendships is with Dr. George H. M. Lawrence, former head of the Bailey Hortorium at Cornell University, who wrote the foreword in this book.

These are some of the people who assisted in writing this book. I am grateful to them all.

EDWIN A. MENNINGER, D. Sc.

Foreword

This volume, *Color in the Sky*, presents the story of flowering tropical trees that today punctuate the Florida skyline, fill interstices with spots of color, and add brightness to a naturally sunny land. But it is more than that, for these trees now enjoyed consciously and subconsciously by so many persons, exist in the Florida landscape, and in other of the warmer areas of this country, because of the vision, concern, and energy of one man—Edwin A. Menninger.

Through this assemblage of articles written over the years, one learns much about the plants themselves, and of their place in the landscape, but more needs to be said of their author for in retrospect he is an unusual man, a man of many attributes, a man of greater accomplishment than most of his readers are aware. Today most of those who know him think of him as a leading horticulturist, a specialist on ornamental plants for the tropics and subtropics, or as a professional writer on these subjects. The facts are that Ed Menninger's acquaintance with flowering trees and shrubs of the tropics began forty years ago when he and his wife first landscaped their new home in Stuart, Florida. Mrs. Menninger asked for color in the trees he would use. This set him on the quest of learning what trees were conspicuous for their flowers, and which ones had a chance of reaching maturity in that Florida environment.

Ed is the "middle" brother of the world renowned Menninger brothers, all sons of Dr. Charles F. Menninger, Founder of the Menninger Foundation, and a long-time physician in Topeka, Kansas, where Ed was born March 18, 1896. The one son who elected not to become a physician, was graduated from Washburn University in 1916 and for two years attended Columbia University's Pulitzer School of Journalism. Before he went to Stuart to become publisher and editor of the newspaper *Stuart News*, he worked six years on the editorial staff of the New York Tribune. With his newspaper publishing in Stuart he developed also a substantial printing business that served the local area.

Early in his studies of flowering trees suitable for the Florida soil and climate he found that it was one thing to assemble a file of data on the kinds to be planted and tested, but quite another when it came to finding even a small fraction of them in nurseries of Florida or anywhere else. For the most part they simply were not to be had. Dismayed but undaunted, and with that determination so characteristic of every good reporter, Edwin Menninger in 1935 took the plunge—he started a nursery where he would grow, test, and evaluate the several hundreds of kinds of exotic woody plants largely known to him then only from the literature. From a raw list of names and often scanty descriptive notes he sought sources from which seeds of each could be obtained. For these he wrote, not to nurseries or seed firms elsewhere, but to men who lived in areas throughout the pantropics where the desired kinds were believed to grow in the wild: to hundreds of botanists (often for precise localities where a given species grew), to foresters, village priests, doctors, lawyers, agricultural explorers, and to housewives. Often he wrote to American consuls in tropical areas for names of local plantsmen to contact about trees and collecting their seed. From these many sources he sought not only their services as seed collectors, but information on the potential of given plants for ornamental use, for notes on the habitat and conditions in which they grew, and for photographs of the trees and their flowers. While no one correspondent would supply all these data, in the aggregate there was amassed one very large central body of information from literally hundreds of sources. This became, unquestionably, one of the largest and most comprehensive of its kind. It helps to explain why a journalist-publisher could become one of the best informed men of all time on this subject of tropical flowering trees.

Tree seeds arrived from every tropical country, but primarily from about five areas: (1) Mexico and Central America, (2) South America, (3) Asia, (4) Africa, and (5) the Australia-New Zealand region and Pacific Ocean islands. Once the seeds were in hand the task only then would begin. Seeds can be tricky to germinate: some must be planted within a matter of hours after removal from the tree (this requires immediate dispatch by air and prompt clearance through customs), others have a built-in dormancy period that may last for months, and many will germinate only when specific conditions of light, moisture, soil, and temperature are provided. These were unknown to Ed when the seeds arrived and success often followed a costly and time-consuming trial and error procedure. From his acquired knowledge he estimated that some 3,000 species of flowering tropical trees could be grown in this country. By 1945 his inventory of saleable trees was sufficient to justify issuance of a catalogue in which some 150 species were offered. Prior to its publication he would promote new offerings through the local press, or in articles he would write for the various nursery or horticultural journals. To develop and encourage interest in the potentials of these trees he gave hundreds of illustrated talks to Florida civic groups and garden clubs. There was understandable resistance from home owners to investment in an ornamental about which they could find nothing in the gardening or landscape literature, and of this Ed wrote (in his handbook *What Flowering Tree is That?*, "We Americans really live our maxim that 'seeing is believing.'" When nurserymen would phone or write him, saying a customer is demanding some tropical tree the nurseryman never heard of, but that was available from Ed Menninger, then did he take special pride in the knowledge of mission achieved.

Whereas most nurserymen make their business their livelihood, Edwin Menninger made his the means of accomplishing an objective: to provide the more demanding home owners, park managers, and civic interests with a source of truly exotic plants that would substantially add to the beauty of the local landscape. His has been an avocational interest transcending all thought of profit, on which from its inception far more has been expended monetarily than has been received. The real profit, the sense of inner satisfaction, is in the knowledge of having made available trees and shrubs and some vines that will continue to beautify the environment long after the present century has closed.

By his own count, Ed Menninger believes he has introduced or reintroduced some 200 kinds of trees to the tropical and subtropical landscape of America. Since individual tastes differ as to which kind is more beautiful than another, the following are among the loveliest flowering trees in the tropics, all introduced, along with many others, by Mr. Menninger:

Alangium Lamarkii	Baikiaea plurijuga
Albizzia Richardiana	Erythropsis Barteri
Bauhinia Hookeri	Calycophyllum candidissimum
Belotia grewiaefolia	Brownea macrophylla
Cassia Brewsteri	Brownea capitella
Cassia leptophylla	Brownea latifolia
Cassia nicaraguensis	Platymiscium trinitatis
Cassia singueana	Michelia Champaca
Cochlospermum vitifolium	Lophanthera lactescens
(double-fld. form)	Securidaca longipedunculata
Dombeya elegans	Hebestigma cubense
Dombeya rotundifolia	Reevesia thyrsoidea
Erythrina Livingstoneana	Mesua ferrea
Gardenia globosa	Millettia ovalifolia
Ixora Finlaysoniana	Dillenia ovata
Jacaranda Chelonia	Vitex altissima var. alata
Kopsia fruticosa	Cordia superba var. elliptica
Kopsia flavida	Eugenia densiflora
Lagerstroemia hirsuta	Eugenia densiflora var. angustifolia
Lagerstroemia Thorellii	Napoleona "cereifera"
Markhamia obtusifolia	Napoleona imperialis
Markhamia platycalyx	Ormosia Krugii
Helicteres Isora	Saraca bijuga
Stereospermum Kunthianum	Tabebuia chrysotricha
Mussaenda erythrophylla	Tabebuia heptaphylla

The nursery enterprise became more than could be maintained as a private avocational operation, and in 1958 it was sold to Stanley Smith, wholesale flower grower who expanded it to occupy some 120 acres.

Accomplishments of the importance of those by Ed Menninger bring recognition and honors in many forms. On April 18, 1964, the Florida State University at Tallahassee awarded him its honorary Doctor of Science degree, at its Spring Commencement ceremonies. It is appropriate to reproduce here the citation accompanying the award. It reads: "Edwin Arnold Menninger, Kansan by birth, Floridian by choice; publisher, printer and horticulturist; recipient of numerous awards; recognized internationally by botanists and horticulturists, your efforts have produced beauty for all to see and knowledge for all to appreciate.

"Among your many publications, *Flowering Trees of the World*, a major achievement in the field of horticulture, is the only comprehensive work on this topic. Our American landscape has been enriched by the more than 100,000 flowering trees that you have grown from seed and distributed to homeowners throughout our country.

"Included among your accomplishments is your work as a journalist, first in New York and later in Stuart, Florida, where, as you have pursued your botanical hobby, you have at the same time devoted thirty-six years to newspaper service.

"You have shown extraordinary qualities of leadership and a capacity for generous sharing of your knowledge to the benefit of the scientific world and to the benefit of all who love beauty in nature.

"By virtue of the authority vested in me by the State Board of Education and the Board of Control and by reason of distinction in service to society, I confer upon you the degree of Doctor of Science with all its rights and privileges."

Earlier, in 1957, the American Horticultural Council (later merged with the American Horticultural Society) awarded him its citation. This reads:

"To you, Edwin A. Menninger of Stuart, Florida for devoting a great part of your life toward gathering knowledge about ornamental plants for the state of Florida. Editor and writer of many articles on tropical plants, your recent book, *What Flowering Tree Is That?* is an outstanding guide for residents and visitors to Florida to become acquainted with the trees that grow in its gardens and parks. Not only have you introduced many new tropical plants, but you have inspired the public to develop a more beautiful Florida through carefully planned landscaping."

In 1958 the Fairchild Tropical Garden, Miami, Florida, gave him its highest honor, its Thomas Barbour Medal. The same year he received also the commemorative bronze medal of the Rio de Janeiro Botanic Garden, issued on the occasion of its sesquicentennial anniversary.

Tragedy struck swiftly and hard just before Christmas in 1966, when from an automobile accident Ed's body was badly broken and the sight of his remaining "good" eye was so severely impaired that no longer can he enjoy the beauty of color in the flowers of the many hundreds of trees he introduced and knows so well. After nearly two years of hospitalization and convalescence, he recovered from the many fractures and bodily damage, and now walks a mile or more daily. But his vision is dim.

At the time this accident happened, he had spent a year gathering material for a new book, *Flowering Vines of the World,* and half of it was written. Later, with 20/200 vision he found he could not read his own notes. Fine and experienced journalist that he was, he could still use his typewriter. Despairing of completing the volume unassisted, he wrote the plantsmen whose friendship he had built up over a quarter-century, and the "miracle" happened. Specialists in Singapore, Australia, South America, South Africa, botanists at the Royal Botanic Gardens, Kew, the Arnold Arboretum in Jamaica Plain, Massachusetts, in Paris, Leiden, and London, wrote the remaining chapters, procured lists of plants, supplied photographs, and brought the work to completion and handed to Edwin Menninger the finished bound volume. Today the *Library Journal* rates it among "The 100 Best Reference Books Published in 1970."

In 1968 the Florida Nursery and Growers Association awarded him their Reasoner Cup, a beautiful silver chalice standing two feet high, and issued in honor of one of Florida's greatest plantsmen of the early part of this century. This came from the Association's recognition of its debt to the man who, more than anyone else, changed its course of direction from one of satisfaction with mediocrity in variety of tropical plants to one of pride in promotion of new and better landscaping through the informed use of superior flowering trees and shrubs. The citation accompanying the presentation of this cup reads. "Annually awarded for outstanding contributions to the ornamental horticulture industry."

In 1971 Menninger was honored by the Massachusetts Horticultural Society with the award of the Society's Thomas Roland Medal for "exceptional skill in horticulture." The citation reads as follows:

"The Thomas Roland Medal to
"Edwin Arnold Menninger. Always a horticulturist at heart, he came to specialize in the importation of seeds of hundreds of varieties of trees and other plants from all over the world, and distributed to Florida homeowners more than 100,000 flowering tropical trees. He is a world-recognized authority on trees for tropical and warm climates and much of the beauty that marks Florida's highways, parks, and gardens, is directly attributable to his enthusiasm, skill, and generosity."

The Thomas Roland Medal is awarded from time to time to men and women who have shown exceptional skill in horticulture. It was designed by Mrs. Oakes Ames in 1927 and was presented that year to Thomas Roland, Nahant, Mass. Its face bears appropriately the representation of a cypripedium orchid, Mr. Roland's favorite.

No account of Mr. Menninger's record of accomplishment is complete without reporting his hundreds of pieces of writing, including these published in book form:

SHADE AND ORNAMENTAL TREES FOR SOUTH FLORIDA AND CUBA. (Joint authorship with David Sturrock, former superintendent of Harvard botanical garden in Cuba.) 1947.

FLOWERING TROPICAL TREES. In Nelson Doubleday's Audubon series, with 38 introduced tropical trees illustrated in color. 1956.

WHAT FLOWERING TREE IS THAT? Illustrated account of introduced trees. 1958. Enlarged edition in 1960.

FLOWERING TREES OF THE WORLD with 425 color plates. 1962.

SEASIDE PLANTS OF THE WORLD. Study of salt-resistant plants. 1964.

FANTASTIC TREES. Trees that are unique in size, structure, or behavior, including many strange, peculiar or downright queer. 1967. Republished *in toto* in the Russian language in Moscow 1970.

FLOWERING VINES OF THE WORLD with 592 photographs, including 200 in color. 1970.

With this publication of *Color in the Sky*, Edwin Menninger brings to all concerned the illustrations of a major portion of his great garden of introductions of flowering trees suitable and often of proven worth for tropical and subtropical landscaping. It stands as an immutable record of his years of study, investigation, and effort in the discovery, introduction, and testing of the plants depicted. With its illustrations appears a text for each plant reporting Dr. Menninger's experience with it, its cultural requirements, and notes on its botanical and landscape features. The volume is a promotion piece, but unlike most of its ilk, it stresses beautification through rejection of the commonplace and substitution of the more beautiful and the exotic. It asks, why accept the drab when the bright and the brilliant can be had for the same effort. It invites the intrepid to explore and experiment, to try plants not common to the area and thus add to man's knowledge of their breadth of suitability and range of adaptability. It is my conviction that no man other than Edwin Menninger could have written this book. All concerned with tropical and subtropical living long shall acknowledge their gratitude for his efforts in the face of physical adversity to place before us the knowledge and experience he has assembled over the years.

1 May 1971

George H. M. Lawrence
President, Fairchild Tropical Garden

1. CRATAEVA RELIGIOSA

2. CLUSIA ROSEA (Scotch Attorney)

Prologue

Flowering trees were so scarce in Florida half a century ago that one in bloom was a curiosity. The landscape held no color at all; it was an intense, unrelieved, year-around concentration of green. In the North the fruit trees and many others provide bright hues in the Spring, and Jack Frost induces intense coloring in the Autumn. To anyone from the North settling down to life in Florida in those days with nothing but an endless sameness of green surroundings all the year, the sharp contrast was staggering and to many, intolerable.

Florida as a whole has almost no showy-flowered native trees. At the southern tip are two beautiful frost-tender trees, the Lignum vitae (*Guaiacum officinale*) which grows too slowly for use in cultivation, and the Geiger tree (*Cordia sebestena*) which is too tender for any except subtropical areas. In 1919 exactly one Geiger tree was growing in a public park in West Palm Beach, and the only Lignum vitae north of Miami were two trees about six feet high at the old Blossom place, a rich man's garden in Palm Beach.

Also it must be recorded that a handful of Royal Poinciana (*Delonix regia*) trees from Madagascar had been planted along Brickell Avenue in Miami, just south of the Miami River, where David Fairchild was establishing the first plant introduction garden for the United States Department of Agriculture. Also around the village square in the settlement of Avon Park in Central Florida, and in a new municipality on the west side of Tampa Bay called St. Petersburg, a few Jacaranda trees (*J. mimosaefolia*) from South America had been planted in gardens. The Southern Magnolia (*M. grandiflora*) is native along the Georgia-Alabama border but for hundreds of miles between there and the Florida Keys, flowering trees in 1919 when I first saw Florida were almost nonexistent.

This is the Florida I saw when I went there to live in 1922; six years later I decided to do something about the monotony of our evergreen landscape. I would plant flowering trees. If one didn't know what to plant, surely he could find out. If plants were not available, one might get the seed to produce these ornamentals. But where? In the process of learning about flowering trees for warm climates and growing hundreds of thousands of them, I wrote fifty-some articles about them and their decorative possibilities to enlist public interest. I needed help in establishing flowering trees in gardens and along the streets and highways of Florida.

Now this book is the story of my horticultural life. My nursery grew from one flower pot to 15,000 containers sitting around the yard, full of strange and interesting trees from every warm country on earth. From contacts made in various ways, it was possible to procure seeds of flowering trees from 200 sources in countries everywhere. Year after year more than 500 kinds of tree seeds arrived and found a germinating spot in the propagating shed. Wooden Coke boxes, made for 24 bottles, were strung with lampwick through the bottom feeding down into gallon cans of water beneath. The box was filled with vermiculite and 24 kinds of seed planted. This rig was placed in a big glass-topped box heated by electric cable to keep the seeds and seedlings warm.

While the seeds were sprouting, I looked up each one in every available reference book. I was determined to know which trees were showiest in flower and which would grow in Florida. Many lists of wanted trees were prepared for every tropical country. It was no use to ask in Kenya for seed of a tree that grows in Brazil.

This tremendous collection of seeds from foreign countries was shared with the United States Department of Agriculture Plant Introduction Station at Coconut Grove, Florida, for the scientists there also got much interested in flowering trees for Florida. This station shared with me the seedlings raised, and also many thousands of plants were distributed to experimenters everywhere.

When the seedlings were well started, they were transferred to tin cans. First came 1,000 gallon cans, then 5,000, then more. Soon the nursery contained an enormous stock of young trees. Seed lists were mailed to thousands interested in plants whose addresses were available. Advertisements were run in nursery trade papers. Annual descriptive price lists of trees coming on in the nursery soon grew into illustrated catalogs. These offered small plants at giveaway prices, often when 3 feet tall or more. Common trees were $1 each or 6 for $5. They were packed in vegetable crates and shipped all over Florida, to Texas, California, Hawaii, and even to the French Riviera. The enthusiasm was contagious, and many Florida nurseries joined in the effort to satisfy the cry of a beauty-hungry public. A few nurseries bought wholesale—one standing order called for 50 Royal Poinciana trees every Spring, year after year.

Advertisements of the nursery always asked the public to come Saturdays or Sundays. They came, tens, then hundreds. As many as 75 people at once sometimes walked around the nursery on Sunday afternoons, money in their hands, all trying to buy flowering trees to carry home in their cars. One enthusiast flew in from Rancho Santa Fe, California, filled his plane with flowering trees, then flew back home again. Two special customers bought one each of every different kind of flowering tree that was growing in the nursery—several hundreds.

The great and the not-so-great came to the nursery to get flowering trees. The David Fairchilds were there; the David Rockefellers flew their own plane from New York and stayed several hours; Arthur Vining Davis came and took a truckload of flowering trees to Miami; Potter Palmer came and took two truckloads to Sarasota; A. W. Jessep of the Sydney botanic garden was there; Harold N. Moldenke of the New York Botanical Garden was there, along with thousands of others including a little girl who wanted a flowering tree to plant by her mother's grave.

Back in 1942–3 I got a bus and ran free sightseeing excursions on Sunday afternoons for soldiers off duty from a nearby army camp and their wives, who were interested in trees and flowers. I travelled over Florida from Key West to Jacksonville and from Fernandina to Panama City, talking to more than 200 garden clubs and showing color slides of flowering trees; these speaking excursions ranged as far north as Pine Mountain, Ga., Charlotte, Highlands, and Hendersonville, N. C., and as far west as New Orleans. Speaking invitations from the Horticultural Society of New York, and combined garden clubs of Houston, Texas were declined as too far afield. A good many garden clubs in

Florida hired busses or organized caravans and came *en masse* to visit the nursery and to buy flowering trees. The Garden Club of my home town obtained several hundred trees and planted them along the streets of Stuart where every year they enliven the landscape with their flowers. The Florida Turnpike Authority bought 200 flowering trees to plant along this highway to Miami. Several hundred trees were sold to garden groups in Plantation, Fla., Lake Worth, Naples, and many other communities where they were planted along the streets. For "The Flowering Tree Man" it was a glorious labor of love.

This book is an anthology of articles written about trees as I learned about them. Much of the information contained in them is not readily available elsewhere, and I know from experience that the complete story as presented herein will be of vast help to others who seek more information about these glorious trees.

The chapters of this book cover twenty-five years of writing for horticultural magazines, the first appearing in 1948 in the bulletin of the New York Botanical Garden. They are printed here just as they originally appeared, including the many inconsistencies. Botanical nomenclature has undergone radical changes, word forms and compounds and even meanings have shifted in that time, but no matter. The reader absorbed in the trees and their possibilities on the landscape will overlook variations and carelessness. After all, the flowers are the things to see.

The flowering trees on Florida's landscape today are the only monument I will ever need.

EDWIN A. MENNINGER

17

3. AESCULUS CARNEA BRIOTTI (Red Horsechestnut)

4. MESUA FERREA

Collecting Plants from World's Tropics
No Hobby for Lazy Man

My interest in showy-flowered trees for Florida gardens dates back almost 20 years when I set out to discover for myself what the world's tropics have to offer in this field. I was surprised to find so few flowering trees in Florida nurseries, until I stopped to think that people will not show any interest in buying trees they never heard of, regardless of how pretty they might be. If the nurseryman is going to live he has to sell what the public wants to buy.

Dr. David Fairchild's four wonderful books about plant immigrants helped to excite my imagination, for this pioneer explorer for plants to grow in Florida has the happy faculty of describing a commonplace plant with words that fairly drip glamor and make every reader want to find one and grow it.

Sitting in an arm chair or holding a book under a reading lamp in bed, I flitted with Dr. Fairchild through a dozen foreign lands, scratched my head over strange plant names that my meagre reference library failed to mention, wondered how successful the author had been in establishing in Florida the scores of plants he talked about.

When I first met him I was shy about asking too many questions, but his generous nature broke down any reserves and we have been fast friends these many years.

To start out for myself on plant exploring expeditions from the depths of an arm chair required a lot of preparation. It was no good asking a man in the Belgian Congo (even if I knew one who was qualified) just to send me seed of a few pretty flowering trees that might be growing in his yard. I had to get books about tropical Africa and read them, selecting those trees that seemed showy in flower and were not in cultivation in the United States.

I had to study the list of 200,000 plants already introduced into the United States, to determine whether I was just seeking tree seeds that greater plant explorers than I had brought in long ago.

Working along these lines might have been simple if only one country were to be considered, but I had made the globe my area to be explored, and slowly I bought books describing the flora of every warm country on earth, insofar as these were available. Laboriously I plodded through their often dull and uninteresting pages, hunting for gleams of light from beautiful flowers that hung on trees.

Now and again I would be rewarded, and I would get out my pencil and make a new index card about some beautiful tree. I have made these cards methodically, many thousands of them as I have waded through literally hundreds of books, and my card library tells where you can find described literally thousands of beautifully flowering trees, any of which might reasonably be expected to thrive in South Florida.

6. METROSIDEROS TOMENTOSA (N.Z. Christmas tree)

5. EUCRYPHIA GLUTINOSA

But getting away from propagation difficulties which are numerous enough to require a book or two, let us talk about plants that do not want to grow after you get them propagated. It seems to me that troubles of this kind fall into several classes:

(1) Plants that thrive in an acid soil but fail in limestone soils, and vice versa.

(2) Plants that resent too much shade or too much sun.

(3) Plants that resent certain kinds of fertilizers.

(4) Plants that resent the slightest disturbance of their roots.

(5) Plants that resent too much moisture.

(6) Plants that just don't want to grow period.

It would be an imposition for an amateur grower like myself to attempt to list any considerable number of my failures in making certain plants grow and a certain sense of humiliation is inevitable in confessing my shortcomings in this field because I have had 20 years actual experience trying to do some of these things I admit I cannot do. But perhaps a review of certain plants that seem to fall in the six classifications above, will help other growers succeed where I have fallen short.

Camellias and azaleas are obvious examples that succeed only in acid soils. The native white-flowered *Tetrazygia bicolor* that grows wild through the woods around Homestead and is now in full bloom, is a good example of a plant that withers away in a soil even slightly acid.

Readers can readily suggest plants like the common Cajeput or Punk tree (*Melaleuca leucadendron*) that die in the shade, or plants like the beautiful purple-flowered Pleroma (*Tibouchina semidecandra*) that die in the sun. And from bitter experience they have made acquaintance with plants that resent certain fertilizers.

I would rather concentrate on the peculiarities of the family of plants known scientifically as Proteas. A common example is the silk oak (*Grevillea robusta*) which grows all over South Florida with no difficulty at all. I can name several others cultivated in Florida without any special care. Yet most of the Protea group are so touchy if their roots are disturbed that they will promptly curl up and die.

I have tried for years to grow those two magnificent Chilean plants, the fire tree (*Embothrium coccineum*) and the evergreen hazel (*Gevuina avellana*), both of which rank among the most beautiful flowering trees in the world, yet my experience with them has been heartbreaking.

I am temporarily more successful with the Australian kin, *Embothrium wickhami* but my fingers are crossed, for out of a hundred vigorous small plants of this species, I have lost 20 in the past two weeks. As I have watched them fade, I have rushed into the breach with fritted elements, iron sulphate, chelated iron and every other weapon I can think of, but the dying process continues.

Six months ago I had a dozen splendid plants of Gevuina, but today only three or four invalids remain. In both instances I transplanted with extreme care into specially prepared soil, but decline began from that time.

Most of the Eucalyptus species resent root disturbance and it is well nigh impossible to transplant a fair-sized tree. The Scarlet Eucalyptus (*E. ficifolia*) which is so widely planted as a street tree in California, is so touchy that

7. MAGNOLIA CAMPBELLII

8. CALLIANDRA HAEMATOCEPHALA

nurserymen always recommend to buyers of the tree to just plant can and all. If they try to take it out of the can they are kissing it goodby.

Fremontia is a beautiful shrub in California, but Florida is too wet for it to grow. Most of the Acacia trees fail in Florida for apparently the same reason. Or perhaps it is because we do not have enough cold nights.

And now to mention some exceedingly beautiful plants which have been failures with me. Megistestegium is a South African mallow that blooms beautifully at the United States Plant Introduction Garden at Coconut Grove, but for me it collapses. I know it resents moisture but it failed without water as well as with it.

I have a score of 4-year-old plants of a pretty citrus relative from the Rio Grande, *Esenbeckia runyoni;* one of them is 6 feet high and the others are 4 inches. I do not know why. I had a hundred fine plants of that magnificent African flowering tree *Baikiaea plurijuga,* but all have died except four and they are puny.

I have failed (and so have others in Florida) with the magnificent African shrub *Sparmannia,* and with that lovely New Zealand white-flowered tree *Entelea arborescens.* I simply cannot grow the national flower of New Zealand, *Sophora tetraptera,* though I have had plants 3 feet high before they keeled over.

I have never succeeded with the lily-of-the-valley tree (*Clethra arborea*), although I have a lot of fine plants of it right now and am still hopeful. I think the most disgusting failure of all has been my record with the gigantic kauri pine from down under, *Agathis australis.*

Out of a hundred seedlings I had four years ago, I still have a dozen. I tell the truth when I report that they are now about 2 inches high, still green, still alive, but that is all I can say.

I could go on with a great list of failures but I have confessed enough. I have 10,000 trees in my back yard now and there would not have been room anyway if all the others had succeeded as well.

9. EUPHORBIA LEUCOCEPHALA

10. SOPHORA TOMENTOSA

So You Think You Have Trouble With Your Plants?

If you pause to review the enormous number of exotic plants that have been introduced into Florida gardens, and check off those that have failed to survive, you can scarcely avoid being amazed at the long list of casualties.

We think we have the ideal climate for tropical and subtropical plants, enough moisture, enough warmth, a variety of soils, and certainly a multitude of experimenters who are willing to devote care and thought to the task. Yet in spite of all these things, there is no gainsaying the fact that the failures are probably more numerous than the successes.

You cannot help wondering what the problems are that remain to be solved. I don't know how our record compares with California—where more than 100,000 exotic plants have been introduced over a period of 75 years, mostly from Australia and South Africa—but I do know by experience that a large number of these newcomers that thrive in California are not being grown successfully in Florida. Why, I do not know.

The difficulties of propagation are known to us all. Because we lack the right insects or bats to pollinate many of our flowers, they set no seed and we are dependent on outside sources. If we get seed from abroad, it often loses its viability in transit. Air layers and mist outfits have helped with certain species, but there are a great many plants that are not being propagated here successfully.

In Trinidad when they want a hedge of Queen's crape myrtle (*Lagerstroemia speciosa*), they stick a row of cuttings in the ground where they want the hedge and water them; bingo, they have a hedge that blooms the same year. You can't do that in Florida. Why? I don't know.

I do know that the Queen's can be grown occasionally from cuttings and less successfully by layers, but what does Trinidad have that we do not? I know also that a lot of trees will throw roots in an air layer but when these are cut off and planted in soil, they die. Why? I do not know.

I have learned by experience that propagating trees from seed is an art. This is particularly true of seeds from abroad, with nobody to tell you what method to use, whether to ripen or plant immediately, whether to soak or dry the seeds, whether to refrigerate or cure.

Reading an Indian book about trees, I ran across a chapter devoted to methods of raising teak trees from seed. "Aha!" thought I, "here is my meat!" All the book said was, it was hard to do.

But one sentence attracted my attention. The author had observed that after brush fires went through a teak forest innumerable seedlings would pop up from the ground. I rushed out to the plant shed, dug up the teak seeds, took them in the house, put them in an old-fashioned corn popper and shook them over the stove burner. "Pop! Pop!" they went.

I carried the seeds back to the seed bed and in two weeks I had 100 per cent germination. The only point to this story is that there is more to growing plants from seed than just sticking the marbles in the ground. Each kind of seed has its own special eccentricities.

11. BROWNEA GRANDICEPS

12. SARACA THAIPINGENSIS

A Flowering Calendar of Tropical Trees in Florida

Flowering trees in subtropical Florida provide a wonderful adventure in world travel along the garden path. Only three native trees* have conspicuous bloom, but several hundred beauties from every tropical country in the world have been introduced to brighten the landscape, and each newcomer has an individuality of its own. To scrape acquaintance with them and try to understand their confusing moods, requires reorientation by anyone who lives in the Temperate Zone where things outdoors are pretty well regulated by the Gregorian calendar, Jack Frost and the groundhog.

To begin with, flowering trees from the warm countries of the earth, arrange their lives quite independent of the calendar. Each tree works out a blooming schedule of its own, probably in response to atmospheric changes not perceptible to man, but little is known of this relationship. The Temperate Zone may sing of "flowers that bloom in the Spring, tra-la," but in lands where there is no Spring, the refrain goes sadly awry. Flowering time is not fixed, even for one particular tree, and some trees under this unbalanced arrangement, may bloom two or three times a year, or they may blossom every month from January to December, like the Horseradish tree (*Moringa oleifera*), or they may just pull back into their shells and refuse to bloom at all. In a few extreme instances, certain trees in Brazil and Malaya, bloom only at intervals of several to many years; who knows what these might do if cultivated in Florida?

Homeowners, puzzled by the reticence of a special "flowering tree" that doesn't flower, often ask anxiously: "Do I need a male tree to make mine bloom?" The answer of course is "No!", first because both sexes are represented in most tropical tree flowers, and second, because a female that feels like putting on a show, can and does bloom spectacularly whether any male trees are "looking" or not.

In a Palm Beach garden in March 1962, a big tree, perhaps 30 feet high with a 40-foot spread, having three trunks, suddenly burst into profuse flowering, the whole top arising from one of the trunks smothered with scarlet blossoms. No flowers at all were produced on the rest of the tree-top arising from the other two trunks. Inquiry proved that the tree had been planted 50 years before by a pioneer Palm Beach resident, long since gone, and it had never bloomed in the memory of his daughter who has lived all her life in its shade. The tree is a monkey-flower (*Flor de Micco*) from Guatemala, known scientifically as *Phyllocarpus septentrionalis,* one of those grown by the U. S. Department of Agriculture from seed collected by Dr. Wilson Popenoe about 1910. These were distributed all over South Florida and many of them persist.

Monopodial blooming is not unusual in tropical trees; The mango (*Mangifera indica*) often has fruit on one branch, flowers on another, new leaves on a third. But how does one begin to understand a tree that, in Florida, waits 50 years to flower the first time, although in Guatemala it flowers when 3 years

(*) The Loblolly Bay (*Gordonia lasianthus*), the Lignum Vitae (*Guaiacum officinale*), and the Geiger (*Cordia sebestena*).

27

13. TECTONA GRANDIS (Teak)

14. NUYTSIA FLORIBUNDA (W.A. Christmas tree)

old in favorable locations, but in other parts of Guatemala it refuses to bloom at all. Why? Nobody knows.

And why bloom in March? In Guatemala the tree blooms in December. Trees that bloom in Australia (south of the equator) in December, should bloom in Florida in June. Sometimes they do; usually they do not. There are no guideposts.

Of course most of the introduced trees in Florida are not as balky as the monkey-flower, and plenty of them bloom exuberantly but without regularity and without reference to the weather, hot or cold, dry or wet. A gaudy assortment of these exotics display their wares all through the year, and in size they range from dwarfs to giants. The colors are a rainbow on the landscape, sometimes for just a few days, again for weeks on end.

Even when both sexes are present in the flowers (as they are on the monkey-flower), many of the introduced trees growing in Florida fail to set seed, for quite a different reason. In the Temperate Zone the bee is thought of as the great pollinating agent, but in the tropics, flowers are fertilized by bats, birds, moths, butterflies, and a lot of other creatures and in many instances a certain kind of moth, etc., is required. This complicates matters. Florida has plenty of insects already, yet the particular one needed to pollinate a certain flower, has not yet arrived from the flower's homeland, and it remains virginal. This business of fertilization reaches an extreme with one Hawaiian plant that depends for pollination on rats. These, in consuming the fruit, brush their whiskers over new flowers nearby that are just coming on.

Places like Singapore, Honolulu, and Cairo have such equable year-'round temperatures that many flowering trees bloom more or less every month in the year, each tree responding to some individual stimulus still undetermined, that may not affect another tree of the same kind in the same place. Visitors to Hawaii find Mexican trees, Indian trees, and Madagascar trees flowering almost any month of the year, although in Mexico, India, and Madagascar, the same trees bloom only at a particular time of the year. Do the steel guitars and Hawaiian moonlight upset these trees and make them go all out? Competitive resorts would like the answer.

Padauk trees (*Pterocarpus* sp.) put on a special kind of performance in places like Singapore. They develop rudimentary flower buds which remain dormant sometimes for weeks. Then suddenly not just one or two, but all the Padauk trees in a neighborhood will come bursting into flower, all at the same time, the same day, like a gigantic orchestra. They get quite covered with yellow flowers, then just as abruptly three or four days later, all the trees quit blooming. Nobody has the slightest idea what causes this gregarious flowering. . Some writers have speculated that maybe a sudden slight drop in temperature, not noticeable by men, pulled the trigger that precipitated the shower of bloom. Then what stops it?

A teak tree (*Tectona grandis*) in the author's garden in Florida developed flower buds all over the top of the tree last January, each bud as big as a pea. They remained there three months without opening, then got tired and fell off. Cold weather was not to blame. What was?

The foregoing recital of a few of the peculiarities of flowering tropical

15. CHAMAEFISTULA ANTILLANA (West Indian Shower)

16. TABERNAEMONTANA ARBOREA

trees is a necessary prelude to a presentation of the outstanding performers to be seen on the Florida landscape. The simplest way to display this floral panorama is by describing the trees briefly in a calendar arrangement. Pick the month you will be in Florida and here are the trees you will see in flower:

JANUARY

West Indian Shower (*Chamaefistula antillana*). Although a vine in its native Puerto Rico, in Florida this is a small tree that blooms right on through cold weather, yellow flowers on the trunk as well as among the branches.

African Shower (*Cassia singueana*). Of the several hundred kinds of "shower" trees, this and *C. nicaraguensis* produce their copious yellow flowers in midwinter in Florida.

Maple Twist (*Pterospermum acerifolium*). This big Indian tree produces 6-inch twisted white trumpet-like flowers among the dinner-plate-size leaves, opening at night, persisting the next day.

Hong Kong Orchid tree (*Bauhinia blakeana*). Spectacular claret-red orchid-like blossoms are produced from November to May.

FEBRUARY

Palmer's Trumpet (*Tabebuia palmeri*). Wine-red trumpet flowers in profusion on bare limbs. This may bloom as early as December, usually blooms several times from January to March.

Geiger Tree (*Cordia sebestena*). Native of the Florida Keys, the Geiger is a repeater, often blooming three times a year, without fixed schedule.

Texas Mountain Laurel (*Sophora secundiflora*). Deep blue pea flowers in clusters have endeared this tree to Texas gardeners. It is often cultivated in Florida.

Lipstick Tree (*Bixa orellana*). Small evergreen tree with flower buds in grape-like clusters, 2 or 3 bright pink blossoms opening at a time, followed by walnut-size pods that are covered with soft prickles. The pods usually reddish green, may be bright orange or golden yellow, and are showier than the flowers.

MARCH

Yellow Silk Cotton (*Cochlospermum vitifolium*). Clusters of gorgeous yellow 4-inch flowers like exaggerated hypericums, at branch tips before the new leaves. A double-flowered form with 5-inch blossoms like golden peonies, originated in Puerto Rico, grows in Florida.

Silver Trumpet (*Tabebuia argentea*). Great clusters of golden trumpet flowers cover the tree before the new leaves. This has been adopted by Sarasota and other Florida cities as their official street tree. Orlando has adopted a somewhat hardier species *T. umbellata*.

Cuban Pink Trumpet (*Tabebuia pallida*). Like the foregoing, this covers itself repeatedly with trumpet flowers ranging in color from shell to deep pink, sometimes on a bare tree, often with the leaves. Much planted as a street tree.

Calico tree (*Calycophyllum spruceanum*). Nearest thing to a "dogwood" performance in the tropics is this tall Brazilian timber tree that decks itself with white bracts in great masses. A similar West Indian species (*C. candidis-*

31

17. MONTEZUMA SPECIOSISSIMA

18. RADERMACHERA SP.

The Flowering Tree Man says: "Tabebuia ipé is the most beautiful flowering tree that I have ever seen. The common name Ipé rhymes with our word café."

Lagerstroemia speciosa (The Queen's Crapemyrtle)

simum) is equally showy in Florida.

Montezuma (*Montezuma speciosissima*). This Puerto Rican tree bears flat 6-inch intensely red "hibiscus" flowers among the 8-inch heart-shaped leaves.

APRIL

Argentine Jacaranda (*Jacaranda chelonia*). Prized in Florida over other Jacarandas because it is dwarf tree, this produces somewhat smaller blue flowers a few weeks earlier than its common relative.

Radermachera (*Radermachera elmeri*). This Philippine trumpet tree produces bushel-size clusters of bright pink flowers that have yellowish throats.

Mother of Cocoa (*Gliricidia sepium*). The common name derives from the practice in tropical countries of sticking a branch of this in the ground beside a newly planted chocolate tree seed (*Theobroma cacao*). The cutting roots readily, produces the shade needed. As a tree this bears quantities of pink (or white) pea flowers so thickly up and down the branches it often resembles an old-fashioned feather boa.

Hebestigma (*Hebestigma cubense*). This is much like the preceding except it flowers with the leaves.

MAY

Flame of the Forest (*Butea frondosa*). Brilliant vermilion pea flowers are set off by jet black, velvety calyces, in the clusters of this small Indian tree.

Pogonopus (*Pogonopus speciosus*). This is suggestive of our flowering dogwood (*Cornus florida*) except the bracts are bright red instead of white.

Shaving brush (*Bombax ellipticum*). Often miscalled "Pachira," the shaving brush on bare branches produced great 6-inch pink, red or white festoons of stamens that look like their namesake.

Red Silk Cotton (*Bombax malabaricum*). Unlike the preceding 20-foot tree, this is an Indian giant to 100 feet and up to 6 feet in diameter, bearing on bare branches 3-inch cup-shaped edible red blossoms.

JUNE

Royal Poinciana (*Delonix regia*). Known in most countries as Flamboyant, this Madagascar big tree swathes its branches with handsome red flowers not unlike gigantic nasturtiums. It is one of the showiest of all trees in flower.

Cannonball tree (*Couroupita guianensis*). A big tree bearing 6-inch complicated red flowers on special stems around the trunk. These are followed by 6-inch round seed pods like cannonballs, that dangle on the stems for months before ripening.

Fried Egg tree (*Oncoba spinosa*). Arabian thorny tree bearing copious white flowers with yellow centers resembling single camellias, followed by 2-inch deep brown golf ball-size seedpods.

Needle Flower (*Posoqueria latifolia*). Tropical American small tree producing quantities of white flowers with 6 inch throats that require a special butterfly to pollinate.

19. CARPODIPTERA AMALIAE

20. TIBOUCHINA URVILLEANA

JULY

Queensland Umbrella tree (*Schefflera actinophylla*). Often a pot plant but outdoors in Florida a 30-foot evergreen tree, producing from the tip of each branch 3-foot plumes of red flowers, long persistent.

Queen's Crapemyrtle (*Lagerstroemia speciosa*). Like the common crapemyrtle except this is tree-like to 50 feet or more with great 18-inch spikes of mauve flowers. One of the most spectacular of all flowering trees.

Hawaiian Hibiscus Tree (*Hibiscus tiliaceus*). A sprawling evergreen tree that in summer covers its top with bright yellow cup-shaped flowers which fade dark red at nightfall.

Tetrazygia (*Tetrazygia bicolor*). Shrub or small tree native to pinelands of lower south Florida, very handsome when loaded with its white flowers. Related to *Tibouchina*.

AUGUST

Jerusalem Date (*Bauhinia monandra*). This orchid tree which often blooms also in March, has bright pink flowers, each tinged at first with yellow margins and crimson polka dots, though everything fades to pink the second day. Despite the common name, it comes from India and does not bear dates.

Tree Ixora (*Ixora macrothyrsa*). In Florida this evergreen small tree bears intensely red phlox-like flowers in 8-inch heads, long persistent.

Purple Glory tree (*Tibouchina granulosa*). This Brazilian to 30 feet covers its evergreen foliage twice a year in Florida (March and August) with bright purple flowers, especially if allowed wet feet as in Cypress Gardens.

Portia tree (*Thespesia populnea*). Small street tree bearing yellow hibiscus-like flowers that fade purple at night.

SEPTEMBER

Horseradish tree (*Moringa oleifera*). Indian tree to 30 feet with roots that do taste like the condiment. Its white flowers among the ferny foliage are reminiscent of a black locust.

Scotch Attorney (*Clusia rosea*). Strand tree to 40 feet with thick spatulate leaves as big as your hand and 4-inch flat white flowers.

Pincushion tree (*Nauclea esculenta*). Dense evergreen African tree whose flowers, the size of tennis balls, consist of 1-inch white stamens stuck all over an interior core which becomes the seed pod.

Broom Melaleuca (*Melaleuca bracteata*). Australian tree to 40 feet with hard black trunk, and evergreen small-needled foliage that makes it look like a conifer till it bursts forth with white bottlebrush flower spikes. Handsomer than the common punk tree (*M. leucadendron*) which is over-planted in Florida.

OCTOBER

Fairchild's Clerodendrum (*Clerodendrum minahassae*). David Fairchild brought this small tree from the Celebes, its white flowers succeeded by very showy red bracts surrounding a blue seed receptacle.

Mountain Pear (*Carpodiptera ameliae*). Only two of these Mexican trees grow in Florida but they are so spectacular in flower that must be included. At flowering time they are covered with 8-inch clusters of fragrant, purple, 5-petalled blossoms.

Goldenrain tree (*Koelreuteria* sp.) Several kinds of this tree grow in Florida, much like those cultivated as street trees through the middle South. Some of the trees in Florida hold their leaves through the winter.

Guie Biche (*Apoplanesia paniculata*). This Mexican tree is still rare in Florida, but when its spreading top is covered with dense masses of white flowers, it looks like a waving field of grain.

NOVEMBER

Colville's Glory (*Colvillea raceposa*). This Madagascar tree bears above the foliage great clusters of brilliant orange flowers that look like bunches of grapes in which each grape unfurls tiny banners of color.

Showy Chorisia (*Chorisia speciosa*). Highly spectacular, this Argentine tree covers its bare branches with 5-inch brilliant pink, 5-petalled flowers.

Perfume Tree (*Canangium odoratum*). The deep yellow 6-petalled flowers along the branches are not showy to the eye, but their intense, delicious odor touches the nose, and makes this the source of many perfume bases.

Dombeya (*Dombeya* sp.) Several kinds of Dombeya are cultivated in Florida gardens, the commonest having upside-down, hydrangea-like pink flowers.

DECEMBER

African Tulip (*Spathodea campanulata*). The stunning big tulip-like vermilion flowers in head-like clusters of this Uganda tree, may appear any month of the year, on different trees in different months.

Red Silk Oak (*Grevillea banksii forsteri*). The glory of Florida gardens through the cool or cold winter season is this 15-foot Australian dwarf tree with brilliant red flower spikes that resemble the clown on a jester's stick, straight out of Shakespeare.

Dwarf Poinciana (*Caesalpinia pulcherrima*). Usually bushy but may be a tree, this evergreen produces fine spikes of brilliant red-and-yellow flowers; all-red or all-yellow varieties are occasionally seen. The related *C. mexicana* with spikes of yellow flowers at branch tips also blooms in winter.

David Fairchild Lives On!

The newspaper headlines say that David Fairchild is dead. But they are wrong. He lives on, a vital force in tens of thousands of hearts, for many who never met him have loved every page of the four books of memories that he left behind, and the Fairchild Tropical Garden is a living memorial that will continue as one of the great cultural centers of Florida as long as people live on this peninsula. Those of us who had the privilege of knowing him intimately will always turn back the pages of memory that are so deeply marked with his enthusiasm for growing things that communicated itself to everyone with whom he came in contact. Life to Fairchild was an engrossing reality, brim full of possibilities, that we humans with our feeble energies can touch and feel and try to understand.

I had met Dr. Fairchild several times and corresponded with him at some length in the first few years of my study of flowering tropical trees, but without really establishing a contact that meant anything to either of us. He knew I was interested in trees and that I was writing some about my experiences with them, but he at first discouraged me in that effort (as he did others) because he had a horror of the misinformation distributed by many would-be horticulturists, and he felt that writers about plants should first be fully conversant with their subject—a huge task in itself. He had a special objection to "common names" for new plants because they do not mean anything and only add to an already confused understanding of the identity of tropical plants being grown in Florida. And so from this great man at first I had only a series of "don'ts" which made me think he must be queer.

But one day I was down at the Montgomery place at Coconut Grove, chinning with my friends, Adolph Jordahn and Ray Vernon, when Dr. Fairchild walked in with a satchel full of seeds he had brought the day before from an exploring trip in Venezuela. He nodded and spoke briefly to the rest of us, then pulled a stool up to the table and started taking seed packets out of his satchel, reading what he had written on each, half to himself, half aloud, opening and examining the contents of each, commenting on the circumstances under which he had collected them, what a beautiful tree or shrub or vine this or that had seemed to him as he remembered it in Venezuela, then going on to another package. This process continued for some time and Jordahn and I were visiting at the other end of the room when suddenly Dr. Fairchild looked up and said: "Menninger, what's this the seed of?" and he passed me some little pea-size black seeds on one side of which stood up a bright blue, fuzzy aril.

I had no idea Dr. Fairchild even knew my name. I still think it was the height of unfairness for a world-renowned plant explorer to pull out of his hat a few little seeds from a foreign land and expect me or any other dub to recognize the identity of the plant from which they came. But I was game so I took my life in my hands, studied the seeds a moment and replied: "*Strelitzia.*" Dr. Fairchild had pen in hand and on an envelope to contain the seeds he started to write: "*Stre—*" and then he stopped and struck a line through the word.

"No," he said, "it's the other genus—*Ravenala*," and he wrote that on the envelope. Then he looked up with wonder and surprise on his face and said to me: "Well, you do know something about this business, don't you?" It is a fact that there are only six genera in that natural order, and Strelitzia has a red aril whereas Ravenala has a blue fuzz. I did come frighteningly close, and that incident cemented a friendship between Dr. Fairchild and me that has continued through all the years. He did many things for me; he sent me seeds, wrote me cards and letters of encouragement and praise, wrote an introduction to my book on "Shade and Ornamental Trees," and even gave me plants, including a *Colvillea* tree that is growing in the parkway in front of C. R. Ashley's house in St. Lucie Estates. Each November when it decks out in gorgeous red flowers I think of my long-time friend. To me it carries a continuing challenge to help carry on the work of acquainting the public with the beauties of the introduced tropical trees. Dr. Fairchild threw me a torch and in my own limited way I shall hold it high to light the way for more and more who love the beauty that the tropical landscape ornaments are unfolding in our Florida.

Three or four years ago I was in Palm Beach one day and learned by chance that Dr. Fairchild was talking to the Garden Club there that day. I went to the auditorium, buried myself in the crowd and listened along with others in rapt attention as the greatest explorer of them all unfolded some of the thoughts nearest his heart, then answered a few questions from the audience. After the show I went up to the rostrum to shake my friend's hand.

"Lord, Menninger, I didn't know you were out there," he exclaimed. "You should have been up here answering all those questions. You know more about these things than I do!"

Wasn't that a gracious thing for a great man to say? I was properly flustered and assured him he had done the job to perfection. But it was characteristic of Dr. Fairchild to share the glory.

I do not mean to leave the impression that Dr. Fairchild and I agreed on everything; in point of fact we disagreed, more or less violently, on several things but we respected each other's opinions. For example, I wrote in one of my articles that there were a lot of trees that nobody should ever plant, and I proceeded to give a list of a few of them which for one reason or another I regard as objectionable trees in any garden. There are weed trees that cannot be controlled, there are trees with nettles and stinging hairs, there are poisonous trees, and some that have flowers that stink (I don't know any other word for it). Dr. Fairchild took me severely to task for my outburst, contending that we ought to grow every kind of tree we can possibly grow so we will know more about them. But I argued in turn that if my experience has taught me certain trees have objectionable features, it is my civic duty to warn others not to waste time on those pariahs but to concentrate on more worthwhile plants. Why should my neighbor spend several years discovering the bad effects I could have warned him about? Dr. Fairchild refused to agree, so we just quit arguing.

I have spent many happy hours on Dr. Fairchild's front porch, talking always at great length about plants. Some months ago when I was in Miami I dropped in at the Kampong (an East Indian name for a plantation), and the

Doctor came out with only a bathrobe on and sat and talked with me an hour or more. He was telling me about new things he was bringing in from the far corners of the world and he was wanting to know about the interesting new things I had found. It was like two boys swapping marbles.

Now I shall see my friend's face no more. But I feel his spirit of encouragement with me as I write this tribute to his memory, and I can hear him say: "Oh, there's so much to be done! Why do you waste a whole column on me? Write about the plants, get people to plant beautiful trees, lovely shrubs, useful plants. Stir them into action. They need to learn, learn. The surface in Florida has only been scratched."

The best way that you or I can express our appreciation for the wonderful job that Dr. Fairchild did as a pioneer in the tropical plant world, is to send $10 for a membership in the Fairchild Tropical Garden, Box 407, Coconut Grove, Florida. It is the only memorial he wanted or needs.

22. KOELREUTERIA PANICULATA (Golden rain tree)

21. EUCALYPTUS FICIFOLIA (Scarlet Eucalyptus)

The Most Beautiful Flowering Trees In the World

The most beautiful flowering trees in the world are to be found in the tropics. In the Temperate Zone grow two score or more very lovely flowering trees, notably the cherries, crabs, and other fruits, magnolias, dogwoods, redbud, and so on, but in the warm areas of the earth more than 3,000 different trees are showy in flower. They create a wealth of beauty, not only in cultivation but in the wild as well, for many of the finest have never been established in parks or gardens. This rich mine of beauty is only beginning to be worked and appreciated.

In the Temperate Zone most of our cultivated flowering trees are hybrids or special forms developed through many years of breeding. Contrast the extensive work done along these lines with the complete absence of a breeding program of any kind with these 3,000 tropical trees. Nobody has ever made the slightest effort to develop floriferous strains of any of them. Add to this the fact that some of these tropical trees have re-crossed in the wild (and in cultivation) until their identity is confused. In Hawaii the *Plumeria* or frangipani is a favorite flower for leis, both because of its fragrance and because it lasts long without wilting. In those islands 67 different forms of this flower are recognized, although probably only two different species are involved, one white-flowered with a bit of yellow in the center, and the other red. This mix-up has resulted from natural crosses, not from any man-made breeding programs.

Persons who live in southern California and in Florida, are familiar with many warm-country trees that have become established there. The African tulip from Uganda (*Spathodea campanulata*), the flamboyant or royal poinciana from Madagascar, (*Delonix regia*), the powderpuff or red *Calliandra* from tropical America, the so-called orchid trees from Hong Kong or India (*Bauhinia spp.*), and many, many others, provide flashes of color in a million American gardens and are no longer thought of as strangers.

Any discussion of flowering trees requires a liberal application of the word "flowers" because in many instances the spectacular display which the tree makes, is not restricted to what a botanist calls the flowers. In the warm Temperate Zone, the dogwood is an example of a beautiful flowering tree in which the true flowers play little or no part. In the tropics the diversity of form of the display is amplified because the colorful, eye-catching parts may be merely masses of stamens (as in *Acacia*), they may be enlarged sepals (as in *Mussaenda*), they may be bracts (as in the poinsettia), and in some flowers which have no petals at all the calyx takes over and can be highly conspicuous (*Symphonia* is an example). Frequently the big show comes from what purists would call the seed pods, which may be far more decorative and colorful than the true flowers (the goldenrain tree, *Koelreuteria,* is an example). A Venezuelan tree called *Ruprechtia* produces great clusters of yellowish-green flowers in among the leaves; these are quite inconspicuous until the sun strikes them; without changing form the flowers turn intensely red and highly conspicuous,

23. ACACIA PYCNANTHA

24. ACACIA VISCOSA

to become with this ripening the seed pods. The showy parts that looked like petals, are now become the long wings on the seed to aid in its dispersal by the wind.

The multiplicity of tree species in the tropics is difficult to comprehend. In and around the city of Singapore grow four times as many different trees as are found in the entire United States. Laymen often gag at scientific names for plants, but how else could botanists differentiate in genera containing literally hundreds of species? What would human parents do if they had 400 children to recognize as individuals?

Consider for a moment the genus *Acacia* with which many are familiar, mostly because cut sprays of it are sold by florists throughout the country under the name of "mimosa." The trees are predominantly Australian, adapted to arid conditions, hence they grow better in California than in Florida. About 500 species have been described, mostly trees, mostly lovely in flower, although too short-lived to come into general cultivation even in suitable areas.

Just because one species of tree is showy-flowered, it does not follow that all species in that genus are floriferous. *Eucalyptus* comprises about 800 different trees and a few shrubs, mostly Australian; of this enormous number, only thirty are noteworthy flowering trees. *Eugenia* is one of the largest genera; more than 1,000 species of trees and shrubs are recognized, yet out of this myriad only two trees can be called beautiful in flower. *Ficus,* the fig family, is largest of all; about 3,000 species have been described, yet they are extremely complicated and synonomy will eventually reduce the number substantially. In this gigantic family, not one of the trees is pretty in flower; it cannot be because the flowers are inside of the fruit!

Of course all trees flower, because this process is the expression of the sex life of the plant, a prelude to the production of seed and a new generation. But in many trees the flowering is neither conspicuous nor colorful, and oftentimes it goes quite unnoticed.

The trees that we call "flowering" are those with floral displays that are the big event of the year, supreme moments of delight, an amazing time at which the trees escape the routines of their existence and become glorified. These are the times that measure the trees' ornamental value, that live in memory, that are looked forward to all the year. To many persons in the Temperate Zone cherry blossoms are synonymous with spring, and nothing welcomes fall so warm-heartedly as the glowing cups of white and gold on the Franklin tree (*Franklinia alatamaha.*)

In the tropics, flowering is not regulated by the Gregorian calendar, nor by the advent of seasons such as prevail in the Temperate Zone, for frequently there are no seasons at all, or the year may be split into wet and dry, or these conditions may follow one another without measurable regularity. Trees cannot be induced to bloom by the application of water, fertilizer, or other chemicals. Actually, fertilizer tends to inhibit bloom because it stimulates the growth of leaf buds at the expense of flowering buds. No tree can be persuaded to bloom by spraying it with a miracle drug. As with all mothers, the desire to produce progeny arises within the tree itself and flowering is the expression of that desire. The particular time of blooming is also selected

26. STEREOSPERMUM KUNTHIANUM

25. COUROUPITA GUIANENSIS (Cannonball tree)

by each individual tree. A few tropical trees produce flowers every day in the year and they may, and some do, continue this phenomenon day after day for a hundred years; to persons living in the Temperate Zone this phenomenon is incredible. Other trees bloom once, twice, or several times a year, not always with the same enthusiasm. At the other extreme some tropical trees bloom only at exceedingly long intervals, up to twenty years or more between flowerings.

Because of infinite variations in the pattern of blooming, residents of warm climates enjoy a parade of flowering trees, the display beginning in January and continuing uninterruptedly, though with varying intensity, through December. It is a never-ending show, and photographs can give only a rough appreciation of the glory of these blossomings.

Flowering trees have many ways of presenting their display. Individual blossoms may be very large and these are particularly effective if set off by a background of bright green foliage. A good many tropical trees produce their flowers on special branches, apart from the branches carrying the leaves. the cannon-ball tree (*Couroupita guianensis*) for example. A large number of tropical trees in the bean family are remarkable for the incredible number of small, bright blossoms which may cover the branches like a locust (*Robinia*) or may literally drip from the branches in *Laburnum*-like festoons. Some tropical trees with fairly large flowers may hang these on strings underneath the canopy so that to enjoy the display one lies on the ground and looks up! Like peach, cherry, and apple trees in the Temperate Zone, many tropical trees bloom when entirely bare of leaves, then renew their foliage. Some tropical trees produce their flowers directly on the trunk or large branches, rather than out among the leaves. Many tropical trees change the color of their blossoms between morning and evening, or from day to day. Some tropical trees produce the male flowers on one tree, the female on another— one of them showy and the other inconspicuous. And then a great many tropical trees simply smother themselves with flowers that individually may be small, or again they may be of good size; either way the effect is spectacular.

With all this diversity, it is scarcely possible to compare the beauty of those on parade. An observer may well gasp at a magnolia blossom a foot across, but as quickly he goes into ecstasies over a blanket of blue flowers adorning a lignum vitae tree (*Guaiacum* sp.), Florida's handsomest native.

Each one of these floral displays therefore has its own claim to beauty and eye appeal. This raises the question of how to define beauty. Can it truthfully be said of any flowering tree that it is the "most beautiful" of all?

Scientists, botanical explorers, foresters, and others interested in trees, who have journeyed to all parts of the tropics and have seen these magnificent trees in their native lands, should be in a position to say which one is the most beautiful: but what an astonishing diversity of opinions they hold! Here are a few of their views:

Thomas Barbour, naturalist, echoed the feeling of many when he called *Amherstia* the most exquisite of all.

Charles Torrey Simpson, pioneer Florida botanist, found *Erythrina* the

27. FAGRAEA SP.

28. DAVIDIA INVOLUCRATA (Dove tree)

finest.

Dr. Harold N. Moldenke, former curator of the New York Botanical Garden, selected the Mexican *Vitex gaumeri* that gets so smothered with blue flowers one cannot see the leaves.

Dr. John J. Wurdack of the Smithsonian Institution, picked *Gleasonia duidana* in Venezuela.

E. J. H. Corner, who was on the staff of the Singapore Botanic Garden nine years, named *Fagraea fragrans* as his choice.

Ernest H. ("Chinese") Wilson wrote that in his opinion, the dove tree (*Davidia involucrata*) is the loveliest of nature's creations.

Austin Smith, a pioneer botanist in Costa Rica, divided his enthusiasm between *Jacaranda copaia* (which is not in cultivation in the United States) and *Tabebuia chrysantha.*

Sir Joseph Hooker, distinguished English botanist, wrote that *Magnolia campbellii* is the most beautiful flowering tree in the world, with *Talauma hodgsonii* a close second. Both these are from the Himalayas.

C. H. Lankester, dean of Central American plantsmen, wrote that the most beautiful tree he had ever seen in flower was a *Lonchocarpus,* "a wonderful soft pale mauve-y blue, feathery dainty foliage completing a floral marvel."

Dr. Wilson Popenoe, greatest of American plant explorers, made famous his admiration of the Guatemalan monkey-flower tree (*Phyllocarpus septentrionalis.*)

Dr. David Fairchild wrote in one of his books that the prettiest flowering tree he had ever seen in his life as a plant explorer, was a specimen in the Celebes jungle of which he never even learned the name! It belonged to the gardenia family.

Most men who know tropical trees are reluctant to make a choice of "most beautiful." They refer offhand to the royal poinciana, the *Jacaranda,* the scarlet *Eucalyptus,* and other trees of outstanding splendor, but refuse to be drawn into making a choice. They have seen so many lovely flowering trees that they hesitate to grade them.

This author's interest in flowering trees was incited 30 years ago by a color travelogue of New Zealand in spring (December). The streets of Christchurch were lined with big trees, each one covered with magnificent plumes of red flowers trimmed in gold—the so-called New Zealand Christmas tree (*Metrosideros*). Nothing could be more spectacular than this tree at the peak of its flowering.

In Florida much of the charm of winter comes from the parade of exotic flowering trees that burst into bloom from November through March, when most of the country is in the throes of cold and snow. Curiously, only one of these colorful trees is a native of Florida, while the rest have come from other tropical regions of the world. However, they have adjusted themselves to Florida conditions where they seem to thrive as contentedly as in their native lands.

In the Temperate Zone, the blooming season in gardens is keyed to the calendar. Thus the cessation of freezing weather is supposed to awaken

30. MORINGA OLEIFERA (Horseradish tree)

29. PHYLLOCARPUS SEPTENTRIONALIS
(Monkey-Flower tree)

the flower buds on the apple trees, just as decreased sunlight in September is the open sesame for chrysanthemums.

What shall we say of a land where freezing never occurs? What hidden power decides when a plant shall flower? What factors govern the growth cycle of a tropical tree? What makes it want to bloom, produce progeny and then perhaps rest a while afterwards? Of course, some tropical trees go dormant and rest before the flowering season, just like their northern cousins, but if there is no cold weather, what makes one tree shed its leaves in November, while another nearby waits until March?

These are only a few of the mysteries of plant life that remain unanswered. Take, for example, the horse-radish tree (*Moringa oleifera*) from India, which flowers continuously every month in the year in south Florida, though it bears seed only in May and June. It is a lovely ornamental when well grown, with locust-like foliage. A number of tropical trees, like *Coumarouna* species, are known to flower only at intervals of six or seven years.

Two winter-blooming shower trees of the genus *Cassia*, both with copious yellow flowers from January to March, stand side by side in a certain Florida garden. One from Central America, Nicaragua shower (*C. nicaraguensis*), produces quantities of seed in three inch thin pods, while Kenya shower (*C. singueana*), a native of West Africa, produces no seed at all. Yet both bloom at the same time, with similar pea-like flowers, though Nicaragua shower is a much brighter hue. The trees are planted less than 25 feet apart, so presumably the same pollinating insects are present.

Landscape designers in Florida are not generally concerned with these mysteries. They simply use the kinds, which experience has shown, will bloom at certain times. Trees which flower in winter are, of course, particularly sought after by residents, who want to enjoy the bloom during their few months residence.

31. GREVILLEA BANKSI (Red Silkoak)

32. APOPLANESIA PANICULATA

Amherstia—Most Beautiful of All (?)

Most authorities agree that *Amherstia nobilis*, native of Burma, is the most beautiful flowering tree in the world. Unfortunately it almost never sets seed, it is hard to propagate by other means, it is a weak-growing thing anywhere except in its native heath, and consequently, like Mark Twain's weather, everybody interested in trees talks about *Amherstia* but nobody does anything about it (successfully). I understand that there are two specimens in the Hope Gardens at Jamaica, and one in the botanic garden at Georgetown, British Guiana, but so far as I know, these are the only trees of the kind in the western hemisphere.

Thomas Barbour told in one of his books, of the several unsuccessful attempts by Harvard scientists to establish *Amherstia* in the Atkins Botanical Garden at Cienfuegos, Soledad, Cuba. He quotes one authority as referring to *Amherstia* without enthusiasm as "just a poor weak thing." The Atkins Garden was abandoned by the University after Castro took over.

Recently I got acquainted with a man who for some years was in mission work in Rangoon, Burma. He is Jesse F. Smith, now alumni recorder at Suffield Academy, Suffield, Conn. I wrote him about *Amherstia*, and he has written so interestingly in reply, I am reprinting his letter.

"I am in position to give you a little help and guidance in your search for information about *Amherstia nobilis*.

"When I first went to Burma early in 1900 my home for the next seven years was in a house in Rangoon known as "Amherstia Place." The most conspicuous object in the garden in front of the house was a perfect specimen of *Amherstia nobilis*, the only one of the species that I saw during my fourteen years in Burma; but during all those years, the tree never failed to produce a profusion of its magnificent blooms. The tree, as I recall, was a spreading, symmetrical tree about 30 feet tall, with a spread of 20 or 25 feet. The bole was perhaps 20 inches in diameter. What the Japanese invasion and the subsequent Allied bombing did to this tree I have not learned.

"I do not recall that my tree produced any seeds; I saw no seedlings; neither do I know of anyone growing it from cuttings, but Bailey's "Hortus Second" says that it is propagated by layerings in the Botanical Gardens in Calcutta, Madras, and Ceylon.

"In Rangoon *Amherstia* grew in the natural gray sandy clay of the elevated tracts of the Irrawaddy Delta, where the annual rainfall averages 100 inches, but practically all of this comes between May 1 and October 1. In Moulmein (Lat. 16° N) at the mouth of the Salween River, the annual rainfall is more than 200 inches. The latitude of Rangoon is 16° 47′ N. The tree is apparently native in the valley of the Salween between Rangoon and Moulmein. The average temperature of this region at 2 p. m. throughout the year is officially stated to be 80° F.

"The *Amherstia* tree is said to have been discovered (i.e. first made known to European botanists) by a Mr. Crawford and Dr. Nathanael Wallich (1787–1854) a Danish botanist who was Director of the Botanical Garden at Calcutta from 1815 to 1854. He first saw it near a monastery in the village of Trochla on the bank of the Salween River, and named it for Lord Amherst, the Governor-General of India from 1823 to 1828, the principal event of whose administration was the First Burmese War (1824–1826) which resulted in the cession of Aracan and Tenasserim to Great Britain."

In 1955 I obtained a dozen *Amherstia* plants from the government nursery at St. Augustine, Trinidad. They were splendid, vigorous little trees and I had great hopes. As required by law, all dirt had been removed from the roots but the trees arrived promptly by air and I replanted them immediately in the best soil mixture I could make. I cared for them tenderly but I had no facilities to maintain high humidity and high temperatures the year around, so the little plants wasted away and died.

33. AMHERSTIA NOBILIS

Canangium—the Flowering Ylangylang
Tops Among "Smelly Trees"

Most tropical plants have flowers that seem to give off no odor whatever. Best known exceptions among those with a fragrance that appeals to man are the Gardenias and Frangipani.

It is probably fortunate there are only a few producing a stench that draws flies to effect pollination: (Some species of Aristolochia, Sterculia, Oroxylum, etc.)

Outstanding among smelly trees to be cultivated in Florida gardens is the Far Eastern Canangium odoratum* which is usually called by the Philippine name that sounds like a streetcar—YLANGYLANG (pronounced E-LANG-E-LANG).

"Perfume tree" would be more appropriate, for the plant has nothing at all to recommend it except the exquisite and pervading fragrance of its unattractive flowers.

The tree itself always looks dilapidated; the wood is brittle and the top and branches break all to pieces in every storm. The branches droop listlessly anyway, the leaves droop, the flowers hang in loose bunches and even the petals are limp.

Instead of the 80 to 100-foot stature attained by the trees in their native Philippines and Malaysia, those in South Florida gardens are rarely more than 25 feet—kept short and often twisted by hurricane winds.

Repeated topping of trees is practiced in Java, the Philippines and Reunion Island where they are cultivated commercially, so that pickers can reach the flowers, for the branches are too brittle to climb.

All through the Far East from the Philippines and Northern Queensland to Burma, Canangium is one of the commonest of evergreen forest trees (there are several species) and flowers for personal adornment come from both wild and dooryard specimens and are sold in shops.

There is no foundation for the native belief in Malaya that the flowers of wild trees are less fragrant. The native manufactures his own perfumed soap by steeping Ylangylang blossoms in warm coconut oil.

(*) The name Cananga odorata adopted by "Standardized Plant Names" is incorrect. Bailey's Standard Cyclopedia of Horticulture explains: "The name Cananga, usually applied to this genus, was used by Aublet in 1775 for an entirely different genus and cannot therefore be valid for the present one. Baillon recognized this fact, and proposed the name Canangium, without, however, coupling it with specific names. It was taken up by Sir George King in his Annonaceae of British India, 1893, and was applied by him to the celebrated Ylangylang tree, Canangium odoratum." Dr. Harold N. Moldenke, curator of the New York Botanical Garden, adds: "There were two genera given the name Cananga. The first was by Aublet in 1775 (Aubl., Pl. Guian. 1:607, pl. 244); the other by Rumphius in 1855 (in Hook.f. & Thoms., Fl. Ind. 1:129). The first of these is now called Guatteria, but this does not change the fact that Rumphius' name is invalid because it is a later homonym of Aublet's name. Your plant belongs in Rumphius' genus and so cannot have the name Cananga. It must take the generic name Canangium proposed for the genus by Baillon in 1868 (Hist. Pl. 1:213). Bailey is correct!"

34. MUSSAENDA ERYTHROPHYLLA

35. CANANGIUM ODORATUM (Ylang ylang)

Commercial quantities of the Ylangylang oil of commerce are produced by steam distillation of the flowers, but steam distillation is not necessary to get the full benefit of the powerfully scented blossoms.

So penetrating is the odor that one flower in a woman's hair is enough and one tree abloom on a rainy evening will send its fragrance over a large garden.

Like most tropical flowers, Ylangylang blossoms send out more fragrance at night than during the day, and the odor is most noticeable when humidity is high.

The individual flower does not lose its fragrance after it is picked; if anything, the odor intensifies and saturates its surroundings as if the petals were blotters soaked in a strong mixture of Hyacinth, Narcissus and Clove.

The name Canangium is derived from the Malay name for the trees—kenanga. The common name Ylangylang occurs in several Philippine languages and is said to mean "something that flutters"—from the pennant-like shape of the petals.

These are six in number, usually one half inch wide and three inches long.

The flowers achieve full size as droopy green clusters along the branches among the foliage, at first almost indistinguishable from the leaves.

Gradually the petals turn yellow, getting darker and darker in color, the fragrance getting proportionately stronger and stronger, until in old blossoms it is too pungent to be pleasant at close range.

Though the flowers are produced in quantities (Macmillan says 20 lbs. of blossoms in a season from a mature tree; Burkill says up to 130 lbs.) they never fall off and litter the ground with a yellow carpet beneath; they seem just to dry up on the branch and blow away as waste.

Exactly how the flowers are pollinated is not known, which may explain in part why the seed is irregularly infertile.

The seed pods, resembling egg-shaped green grapes in clusters among the leaves, turn black before falling off.

The pods vary in size from one quarter to one inch long, contain up to a dozen black grape-like seeds.

The Ylangylang flowers twice a year (October and March in Florida), continuing to develop over a long period of weeks or even months so that flowers and seeds appear on the tree at the same time.

Although most trees bear quantities of seed, no seedlings appear on the ground around them and nursery propagation is uncertain; consequently the trees are rather scarce.

Seedlings begin to flower when two years old, and from 18 to 24 inches high.

Belonging, as Ylangylang does, to the Custard Apple family (Annonaceae), it is not surprising that the fruits are relished by poultry, pigeons and other birds. The wood of the tree however is definitely unattractive to insects.

Lawsonia—Henna—Its Fragrance and Color Are Ageless Lures

A shrub which has been a garden favorite for three thousand years must have exceptional merit. Such is the record of the henna plant (*Lawsonia inermis* L. = *L. alba* Lam.) which Solomon was lauding when he wrote, "My beloved is unto me as a cluster of camphire in the vineyards of Engedi."

Solomon, of course, cherished camphire for its delightful, penetrating fragrance which masked less desirable odors in the harem. But fragrance is only one of the good points about the henna plant that endear it to many.

Henna is native from northern Africa to Madagascar, and from Iran to India and Australia, but it is now cultivated or gone wild in all warm countries. In Egypt it is a crop; seedlings are transplanted into the field two feet apart, irrigated regularly, and the branch tips harvested twice a year for the leaves. The plant thrives about twelve years under this regimen, then it is cut off near the ground and allowed to grow anew.

Gardeners like henna because it makes a good hedge plant. It grows readily from seeds or cuttings, transplants easily, submits to many abuses including neglect, and the small, opposite, shining leaves respond well to shearing. Periodic pruning stimulates flower production. A thrifty plant bears resemblances to some forms of privet (*Ligustrum* sp.). The epithet *inermis* in the plant's scientific name means thornless; but sometimes in poor soil or under difficult growing conditions, spines do develop among the leaves on the branch tips. Henna will grow in very dry areas, though it becomes more luxuriant with ample moisture. It will even grow in salty soils where so many other plants fail.

The fragrance of the flowers makes the plant highly desirable to the perfume industry, and in the Near East it is utilized in embalming. The flowers, in dense, twelve-inch panicles at the tips of the branchlets, have four petals which ordinarily are greenish white, but sometimes these are bright, creamy white. A yellow form and a variety with cinnabar-red petals are known, and in Calcutta occurs a beautiful form with clear pink flowers. The eight stamens greatly exceed the petals in length and are the most conspicuous part of the flower. The flowers do not last long after being cut for bouquets.

The flowers are followed by quantities of round seed pods, the size of a pea, which weigh down the branch tips. These are first green, then red, finally dark brown, splitting open irregularly, as is often the case in the crape-myrtle family (*Lythraceae*). Sometimes the unopened seed pods persist on the plant until the next flowering period.

Henna is best known for the dye obtained from the leaves and used extensively in shampoos, rinses, brilliantines and the like to give the hair a rich auburn tint. In North Africa, Asia Minor, and India henna is used to dye the nails, the palms of the hands, and the soles of the feet an orange-red; this practice is supposed to make the women more beautiful. In some places, particularly Iran, this practice is not confined to women but is also followed by men. Henna is used in the Near East to dye the heads of children, the beards of men, and the manes and tails of horses. In dyeing beards, the henna rinse is followed by indigo, which turns the hair a beautiful jet black. Using henna to dye the nails is a very ancient custom, for Egyptian mummies were commonly thus beautified.

To make the dye, the dry leaves of the plant are pounded to powder, then mixed with a little hot water and some sticking agency, such as lime or catechu. This paste is applied to the part to be dyed and left overnight. The color lasts a long time.

For centuries medicine men have had a heydey with henna, using it as a remedy for everything from leprosy to rheumatism. For an array of these uses see Burkill: *Dictionary of the Economic Products of the Malay Peninsula.*

Religious uses of henna are many. Buddhists strew the flowers as offerings to their deities. The Jews have used them in baths and in other ceremonies.

Henna has many common names. In the Philippines it is called *cinamomo*. In the West Indies it is Jamaica mignonette or the mignonette-tree, because the flowers resemble those of the true mignonette (*Reseda odorata* L.). In Mexico reseda is used as a common name, and elsewhere the names of Indian privet and Egyptian privet are often heard.

Henna is usually seen as an upright shrub four to six feet high, but in India it is sometimes a straggling tree to twenty feet. Linnaeus named the genus after John Lawson who, in 1709, published an account of his adventures in North Carolina. These ended rather abruptly three years later, when he was burned at the stake by the Indians.

36. LAWSONIA INERMIS (Henna)

38. ROBINSONELLA CORDATA

37. GREYIA SUTHERLANDII

ROBINSONELLA—A Tree With Blue Hibiscuslike Flowers

When something new and different turns up in the plant world, there is always a flurry of excitement and a mad rush to obtain plants. Southern California experienced just such a thrill this spring over the spectacular blooming performance of two trees in front of the residence of Mrs. John W. Harris, Los Angeles.

The trees, 15-20 feet high and as much across, were moved to their present location in November, 1951, and flowered sparsely the following spring when they were identified by Miss Mildred E. Mathias of the division of botany, University of California, in Los Angeles. Scientific name of the tree is *Robinsonella cordata,* and the flowers make you think of Hibiscus, except that they are small, mostly in dense clusters, and bright purple in color.

This past February and March, both trees flowered profusely, giving a "blue cloud" effect, and all Los Angeles flower lovers went wild. They grew wilder when they discovered that no plants were available, and they would have to wait till the nurserymen could grow some. The nurserymen are industriously doing just that, and have even sent hurry calls to Guatemala for propagating material. The flowering this year lasted about a month in spite of severe drying winds which doubtless shortened the flowering time.

We in Florida who have gone into such rhapsodies over the wonders of the Chinese Hibiscus and its spectacular hybrids, may be a little startled to read Dr. Paul C. Standley's conclusion that Robinsonella stands out "among the most beautiful of The Malvaceae, their white or bright purple flowers notable for the delicacy of their coloring rather than the gaudiness that characterizes many members of the family."

The genus *Robinsonella* consists of six species of large shrubs or small trees restricted to the mountains of Central America. There are three species in Guatemala, one with white, one with purple, and one with purple-veined white flowers. Writing in "Tropical Woods" about Guatemalan trees, Dr. Standley says:

"The plants sometimes occur in abundance locally, usually on brushy sides of deep canyons, and when in flower the trees, sometimes as much as 10 meters high, are visible from a long distance. All species of *Robinsonella* are well worthy of cultivation in regions of suitable climate, which should be rather cool and fairly moist. The most attractive of local species is R. *divergens* of Verapaz, Santa Rosa, and Huehuetenango. There are handsome individuals of this species in gardens in Coban. They are a beautiful sight when in full bloom in March and April, being covered with small clusters of pendant, bell-shaped flowers whose ground color is white but so strongly veined with bright purple as to appear more purple than white.

"The blooming season of *Robinsonella* is from December to April. Although some are shrubby, mostly the plants are seen as slender trees to 20 feet. One white-flowered form is cultivated in the gardens and parks of Huehuetenango.

The species that has come into cultivation in California is *Robinsonella cordata*. Although originally reported from Mexico, it extends in the wild to Guatemala. It blooms in December and January, well ahead of the other species and "during its brief blooming season, is an exceptionally beautiful tree on account of its profusion of bright purple flowers." Dr. Standley continues: "During the flowering season the trees can be recognized at a great distance because of the masses of brilliant and distinctive color. Like all other members of the genus this tree is a handsome one and well worthy of cultivation."

The flowers of *Robinsonella* are sometimes in small clusters on short branchlets, but often are in rather large dense panicles. For those persons who feel that every newly introduced plant should have a "common" name for ease of handling, some comfort may be derived from the fact that in Guatemala the natives sometimes call this tree "Chaqueta de Novia" and again they call it "Amapola grande." It would seem somewhat easier just to stick to the lilting scientific name *Robinsonella*.

The history of the California trees is interesting. Miss Mathias writes: "In 1939 Russell Westcott (now on a ranch in the Vista area, and no longer active in horticulture) was sent to Guatemala by Paul J. Howard's California Flowerland. In the Sierra Madre near Quezalpenango he saw the trees in full bloom. Cuttings were procured and sent to Los Angeles by air. They did not root but sprouted and the sprouts were rooted. They were grown at the nursery in West Los Angeles but never flowered, probably because the nursery is in a colder area. Two plants were put in the county park in Long Beach but their fate is not known at present. Cuttings were given to Evans & Reeves.

"The two trees in Bel-Air were moved there from the nursery to Bel-Air in 6 foot boxes, since they were the only two known to be in the country and every precaution was made not to lose them. Side boxing was started in May, 1951, with root pruning on two sides, back-filling, and a wait for recovery. The other two sides were then similarly treated, and finally the bottom boxed. It is now known that they are easy to move and probably would have recovered if bare-rooted."

Morgan Evans of the nationally famous establishment of Evans & Reeves, West Los Angeles, wrote me:

"The two trees near here flowered generously this year, I think perhaps the best flower they have ever produced, as it created a mild sensation. I may have a few plants of this specie, but I can not determine for sure, as they are only about 2 years old, and it is not possible to positively pin down the identity from the seed source. The botanists can only tell us that it appears to be the same thing but might turn out to be a white flowered form, for example. I have written to several friends in Mexico and described carefully the species which we are interested in, and I am keeping my fingers crossed in the hope that seed will be forthcoming of this blue one.

"I can't believe that the *Robinsonella* trees have been flowering profusely until this season, else there would have been more recognition ere this. I consider them quite an addition to our all too-few, flowering, evergreen trees in southern California. They are growing in a fairly warm situation, yet I suppose received temperatures of about 26 or 27 degrees in 1949, as the *Ficus utilis* across the street was superficially damaged in that year."

The Beautiful Peltophorum

The finest trees for spreading, quickly grown shade in Florida and quantities of pretty yellow flowers all summer, are known botanically as *Peltophorum*. Unfortunately they are sometimes carelessly called "Yellow Poinciana," which ignores two facts: (1) there really are such things as Royal Poinciana trees with yellow flowers; and (2) *Peltophorum* is only distantly related, and if it is to be christened with a common name, it should be one that is more appropriate.

For the time being, it might be well to retain the name *Peltophorum* for everyday use, and you can pronounce it Pelto-Forum, or you can follow the book rules of pronunciation and call it Pel-TOPH-o-rum. What matters the pronunciation if you can make the tree grow in your yard?

There are two principal kinds of *Peltophorum* in common cultivation in Florida. Best known is *P. inerme*, a very large, umbrella-shaped tree from the Philippine Islands, sometimes 150 feet high in its native land, with great spikes of yellow flowers all over the top of the tree from May to August, made more conspicuous by the dense, heavy green foliage behind them. *P. inerme* is also known as *P. ferrugineum* and *P. roxburghi*. One of the best descriptions of this tree appeared in Kathleen Gough's *A Garden Book for Malaya*. She wrote:

"Best of all for cuttings are perhaps the luminous flowers; those that glow and hold light. I not know what it is that gives some flowers a 'lit-up' look; not only does the light shine through their petals, but they seem to catch, reflect and hold it . . . Yellow and flame-colored dahlias hold light, and so do the fleeting single hibiscus, blue morning glory and, above all, the golden spikes of *Peltophorum inerme*.

"Sprays of these flowers indoors seem liquid gold; they are wonderfully beautiful with their decorative unopened tight bronze buds and bronze stems, just touched with gilt. The fully opened flowers have crinkled golden petals and orange-tipped stamens. The light shines and glows in a mass of these beautiful flowers more intensely in the shade indoors than when they are growing outside."

Dr. Henry Nehrling wrote of the *Peltophorum:*

"In comparison with the many other distinguished representatives of its family, this tree adds variety to the collection, its compound leaves being much larger, individually and collectively, of a much deeper green, showing in certain lights a faint steel-blue tint in the old, and a more ferruginous cast in the young foliage. The large, erect flower panicles terminating every shoot are covered with a rusty-brown tomentum with a slight touch of chestnut color. Its vigorous growth, the distinct green color of its foliage and the large erect panicles of bright yellow, fragrant flowers continue to make this tree a marvelous object of tropical beauty. It is a unique and a first-class flowering and shade tree. It thrives well in South Florida, is evergreen, not too dense, gives a good shade and produces an abundance of showy flowers. A well drained soil, rather dry, is what it requires."

The other *Peltophorum* frequently seen in Florida is native of Brazil and is called *P. dubium,* which is a synonym for *P. vogelianum.*

39. PELTOPHORUM INERME

Spathodea—the African Tulip

Imagine a tiny rounded bunch of bananas the size of a baseball, except these are not bananas. They are flower buds, each the size of your little finger, reddish brown, massed together at the end of a heavy leafy branch. Suddenly half a dozen of those fingerlings on the outside of the bunch, split up and down, and from each one pops a brilliant scarlet flower that much resembles the finest tulip you ever saw, often three inches across and five inches deep.

The lip of the flower all around is yellow, and the inside of the cup is yellow with red markings. The whole outside of the ball is cluttered with these huge red flowers and they hang on for several days. As soon as one is spent and falls to the ground, carrying the remains of the bud with it, another fingerling splits open to fill the void, and the cluster thus continues to bloom over a long period, often a month or more.

This spectacular flower display marks the African tulip tree, originating in Uganda, but so easily propagated and growing with such rapidity, it is now pantropic and may be seen in warm countries everywhere.

One of its seed pods which is flat and about the size of your hand, often contains 500 tissue-papery seeds; fortunately the seed pods, standing erect at the branch tips like Christmas candles, are produced only occasionally or the tropics might be overrun with African tulip trees. The plants themselves grow very fast; six feet in a year being not unusual, and like most fast-growing things, the wood tends to be soft and brittle.

This tree is not related to the forest monarch of the Temperate Zone in North America which is frequently called "tulip tree" or "yellow poplar," with its handsome, bitten-off leaves and yellowish, tulip-like blossoms that carpet the ground beneath in Spring.

Because the African tulip tree is frost tender, it is often frozen to the ground by 30-degree temperature in Florida, if of long duration; and because the wood is brittle, it often shatters in high winds. But by neither of these catastrophes are the roots bothered, and the tree springs back from the ground almost immediately and may flower again the same year.

The handsomest tulip tree I ever saw was a huge bush 20 feet high and 20 feet across, every branch tipped by huge flower clusters; it resulted from a hurricane breaking off an old tree near the ground. The owner let it sprout again as it would, and the effect was breath-taking.

Nobody knows much of the sex life of an African tulip tree. It may bloom any month in the year, and the same tree frequently produces two or three crops of flowers. Most trees set no seed at all, ever. But a seed tree, one that occasionally decides to produce a family, may form only two or three pods one time, another time it will go wild with joy.

I have watched a 40-foot tulip tree near my office window for some 25 years. It is a magnificent specimen and blooms a lot, but with all my watching I have never seen seed pods on it but once, and that time it was covered with literally hundreds of them from top to bottom. Like all the members of the Trumpet

Creeper family, both sexes are present in all the flowers of the African tulip tree, but that does not mean that fertilization will take place even if the proper pollinizing agent is available. Flowers, like people, have moods.

The African tulip tree thrives on any kind of soil, but it requires full sun to bloom. Occasionally a tree is planted in the shade, and it will grow there, but it shoots up quickly to exceed the leafy canopy that is preventing the production of flowers, and frequently you see tulips 50 feet high, overtopping everything else and blooming their hearts out against an azure sky.

The trunks of old tulip trees develop buttresses and the bark which was smooth at first, grows ridged and scaly. To the Temperate Zone dweller, the leaves of the African tulip look a lot like an ash, except they are bigger, often two feet long, and sometimes hairy. And, of course, the tulip is evergreen, new leaves replacing old so gradually that the period of change passes quite unnoticed.

40. SPATHODEA CAMPANULATA (African tulip tree)

64

Spathodea campanulata (The African tulip tree)

Spathodea campanulata Cv. (The Yellow African tulip tree)

The Yellow African Tulip Tree

Brand new to American horticulture is the simultaneous appearance in Florida and Hawaii, of a yellow-flowered form of the African tulip tree (*Spathodea campanulata*). This tree is not related to the American tulip tree *Liriodendron tulipiferum*.

The African tulip tree with evergreen foliage and clusters of brilliant red, or red-fringed-yellow, tulip-shaped flowers, is deservedly popular in Florida, Hawaii and other warm areas because its spectacular flowers appear above the foliage, blooming over a period of several weeks, and repeating the process two or three times a year. The flower buds come in banana-like bunches as big as a turkey egg. The outer buds push forth their flowers first, and as these flash in the breeze a few days and then fall away, they are replaced by other opening buds, a beautiful, continuing process. Each tulip-shaped flower is as big as a man's fist.

Now comes the excitement. After being grown in South Florida and Hawaii for more than fifty years, suddenly in both places appeared a tree with magnificent, golden yellow flowers. Nobody in this country had ever seen anything like them. The new tree in Florida was at the U.S.D.A. Plant Introduction Garden in Miami, where it is known as H-21575. The other appeared in the MacKenzie Nursery at Kailua-Kona, Hawaii. Both bloomed first in September 1972 and both are being propagated by root suckers. This author recently received seed of the Hawaiian tree and also of the biggest yellow-flowered tree at the Greensmith Nursery in Nairobi, Kenya, and turned them over to the Fairchild Tropical Garden at Miami to propagate; unfortunately, it is unlikely that more than a few of them will produce yellow flowers, but nobody knows till he tries.

Where and when did the yellow form originate?

J. B. Gillett of the East African Herbarium (East African Agriculture and Forestry Research Organization), at Nairobi, Kenya, writes in this connection:

The only definite published statement which I know of concerning the yellow flowered form is in Eggeling & Dale: *Indigenous Trees of Uganda* ed. 2 (1952) p. 42 "A form with rich buttercup yellow flowers, well worth perpetuating, occurs in Bugishu and a somewhat similar tree has been found in Mengo." No such remark is in the first edition of this work (1940) so one may perhaps conclude that the yellow form was found after 1939 and certainly before 1952.

A leading amateur gardener in Kenya like H. M. Gardner who was for long chief conservator of forests in Kenya, has told me that the yellow form occasionally cultivated in Kenya is derived from the Uganda plant. He also told me that what he thought was the sole known wild tree had disappeared. The yellow form is simply called that with no special name.

Mr. Gardner (very vigorous at 83) tells me that a farmer called Arthur Barnley farming in the Cherangani hills, N.W. Kenya, found the tree in Uganda c. 25 years ago and obtained a root sucker from which he established a tree in his garden from which in turn a few people in Kenya have obtained suckers. Mr. Gardner does not know of anyone trying to grow it from seed.

This is the same Mr. Barnley who is quoted in the 1962 edition of Menninger: *Flowering Trees of the World* (with color illustration) as follows:

Tulip trees with pure yellow flowers are extremely rare. Arthur W. Barnley, P. O. Box 332, Kitale, Kenya Colony, sent the author a koda-chrome slide (Plate 39) of the yellow form with this note: "I took many photographs before I got the color right. I have distributed seed of this form but have not yet heard of anyone's success with it. The only sure way of propagation as regards accurate yellow color is by root cuttings."

Peter Greensmith, commercial nurseryman of Nairobi, Kenya, writes of early acquaintance with the yellow form:

Sometime around 15 years ago an old friend of mine saw a yellow flowered *Spathodea* in a semi-forest area of Uganda, near Kampala, and dug up three plants from beneath the tree; these may well have been root suckers. These three trees were grown on my friend's farm on the Cherangani Mountains in Western Kenya and my original tree was a root sucker. However as soon as my tree and those of other friends seeded we started growing them from seed and I have sent the seed to contacts of mine all over the world.

The origin of the yellow form in Hawaii is told by Mrs. Barbara MacKenzie of the MacKenzie Nursery, as follows:

A friend of ours, L. W. Bryan, retired forester, had a friend, Dave Barry, Jr. who brought back some yellow African tulip trees from Greensmith's nursery in Nairobi, Kenya, in September 1970. Five of the seeds germinated and he brought them to us to plant and grow. Of the five, four came out red and one came out this beautiful golden color.

Before we transplanted the tree out of the 10 gallon container, two roots had gotten out and were shooting up young plants. We have been taking slips off of these and starting new plants from them in our mist room.

Some variations in the yellow color are noted by these authorities. Mrs. MacKenzie writes:

"In our nursery the color is a beautiful warm gold. I am enclosing a slide of it but the color is not exactly accurate. The closest way I can describe the color is to say that it is exactly like the color picture of the *Zantedeschia elliottiana*, page 139 in our Exotica 3."

Because both the Hawaiian and the Florida trees were received as seed of *Spathodea nilotica,* it is important to emphasize here that this name is synonymous with the commoner name *S. campanulata,* and it is not a new or different species. Confusion has long existed over the names. Noel Y. Sandwith of the herbarium at Kew, long outstanding authority on the Bignoniaceae, wrote this author 20 years ago that he regarded the two names as synonyms.

Al Gentry, assistant curator of the Missouri Botanical Garden at St. Louis, now recognized as a leading authority on this family, writes:

I agree with Sandwith that they should be regarded as synonyms. Even were they not to be considered synonymous, the yellow-flowered form could hardly be identified with *S. nilotica* any more than with *S. campanulata.*

I had never heard of a yellow-flowered form of *S. campanulata.* Although I cannot say for sure, having never seen a specimen of this plant, I am reasonably certain that it is only a cultivar. I have seen it pure red (that is without the yellow border). Although I have not looked at the full pigmentation of the plant, I would guess that its normal red-orange flower color is due to two separate pigments, one yellow, the other red. Presumably a single gene mutation would be all that would be needed to prevent formation of the normal red pigment and this would result in a pure yellow flower. It seems probable that this is the explanation of the yellow-flowered form which should then be treated as a cultivar. Of course, it is quite possible that such a mutation could have occurred independently in a number of instances.

As to the prevalence of the yellow-flowered form, it would seem to me unlikely that it is known outside of cultivation. There are quite a number of Bignoniaceae with two color forms known from nature, but most of these are typically lavendar-flowered type with an occasional white-flowered individual. I suspect that in red-flowered species like *S. campanulata* (i.e. bird pollinated) a yellow-flowered form would be at quite a selective disadvantage, although such allegations are very difficult to prove.

Mr. Gillett of the East African Herbarium writes:

We now incline to the view that *Spathodea nilotica* is not specifically different from *S. campanulata* though I am not aware that anyone has studied the question really thoroughly.

Mr. Greensmith writes on this subject:

I think that you are correct in stating that *Spathodea nilotica* is synonymous with *Spathodea campanulata.*

Dr. Russell Seibert, director of Longwood Gardens, Kennett Square, Pa., writes of his part in the drama:

Yes, I had a bit to do with stimulating the introduction of the yellow *Spathodea* into the U.S.A. In 1963 I visited Peter Greensmith and asked specifically that seed of this be sent to us when available. As a result our introduction card indicates:

70974—*Spathodea nilotica* Coll. August, 1970, from a yellow flowering tree. Rec'd. as seed 9-16-70 from Mr. Peter Greensmith. Horticultural Consultant. Langata, 586, P. O. Box 604 Nairobi, Kenya. Later, plants were distributed: as plants—1 sent to USDA Introduction Garden; and later 3 more sent to above. As plants 3 sent to Fairchild Tropical Garden. As seedlings also sent to Parrot Jungle, La. Tech. Univ., Marnier Lapostol, France, Fantastic Gardens, Calif. Jungle Gardens, Foster Gardens Honolulu, Hort. Bot. Bogor, Indonesia.

We still have one plant here which so far has *not* flowered. This is not unusual as only on one occasion have we ever had a *Spathodea* put out a bloom under glass, and it was a poor representation of the genus.

Seedlings were also sent to Miami and also distributed on our surplus plant list which would account for Dave Barry having it.

David Barry, Jr. writes that he has never seen the yellow *Spathodea* in bloom. His letter continues:

When Peter Greensmith sent me seeds I turned them over to my good friend, Co. L. W. Bryan, of Kona, who gave them to MacKenzie to grow. At the time of sending the seeds Greensmith said that the seeds of this species can not be depended on to produce yellow flowers.

I have a single plant in my nursery that I plan to send to Honolulu later this year to be planted near my home. I believe it was sent to us by Longwood Gardens.

Seeds of the yellow-flowered form have been received three times in recent years at the Plant Introduction Station in Miami, and all of these originated at the Peter Greensmith nursery in Nairobi, Kenya. The first of these was received from this author in December 1970 and the number M-21575 was assigned to it. Four plants of this in Miami, and one in the parking area at the First National Bank of Stuart, Fla., have reached heights up to 8 feet but have not yet bloomed.

Another shipment numbered M-21664, was received in April 1971 from Longwood Gardens, Kennett Square, Pa. One of these bloomed bright yellow in Miami last year.

Shipment M-22185 was received in March 1973 but none of these has flowered yet.

Dais—A Daphne Relative

The garden lover in Florida who is on the lookout for a new and unusual shrub worth cultivating for its beautiful flowers, should give a spot to a South African native called *Dais*. It is cultivated down there all the way from Natal south and it is hardy enough to thrive through most of Florida.

Dais cannot be had or grown in Florida without vigorous effort, but once established it is just as pretty as the garden shrub *Daphne*, over which northern flower lovers go into ecstasies. These related plants belong to the natural order Thymelaeaceae, commonly called the Mezereum family, which is not represented by any showy-flowered plants on the tropical landscape except for a tree *Daphne* in Malaya, and a white-flowered Peruvian tree called *Schoenobiblus*.

Plant explorers have reported six species of *Dais* in South Africa and Madagascar, but *D. cotinifolia* is the only one in cultivation. In the wild it is frequently a tree of 20 feet, but as so often is the case, in cultivation it is an evergreen shrub of eight or ten feet, beginning to flower when it is two to three feet high. It has been cultivated in English greenhouses since before the American Revolution, and it is seen frequently in California gardens, where it seems to thrive with very little moisture. It is however, only rarely grown in Florida gardens. Perhaps the fact that it is rather a difficult plant to propagate has some bearing on its rarity here, but it is a highly attractive plant that is worth trying for. It appeals particularly to those persons who like fragrance with their flowers, for in this field *Dais* excels.

The individual blossoms of *Dais* are about one-half to three-quarters-inches across, with five spreading narrow lobes and ten stamens. These are a pale lilac in color, or perhaps you might call it a delicate pink. The flowers are clustered in umbels that are very dense, up to three inches across. With their long stalks they look for all the world like white torches—and the name *Dais* really means "torch." The clusters of bloom come on the tips of the branches and they light up the whole plant.

Dais blooms in June and July in South Africa, over a period of several weeks, but in California and Florida it carries its flowers into September. It is worth noting that although *Dais* is reported as evergreen in South Africa, it is briefly deciduous in a Florida garden and apparently so in California.

In Natal, the bark of *Dais* is said to yield the strongest fibre known to the natives of that country and they use it to make thread.

41. DAIS COTINIFOLIA

42. ALEURITES MONTANA (Mu oil tree)

Flowering Trees for Colder Areas

What Florida homeowners most need right now is to get acquainted with some of the outstandingly beautiful ornamental trees that will survive sudden temperature drops.

To see a much-loved flowering tree in a garden, raised with years of care and effort, killed by winter's fiercest overnight effort, is discouraging. Perhaps at the same time it should be a warning that it behooves us to learn about pretty trees that are somewhat hardier and expend special efforts to get such established in our home yards.

It is not going to be easy to get these, or to get them established, or to await their maturity, but if we fail to make a start somewhere, we can scarcely expect somebody else to fill the void for us.

Most of the trees to be described are trees most Floridians have never heard of.

Does that matter? It is important that we start getting acquainted with them, because they are the ornamental trees that will survive the kind of climate that prevails here.

Australia offers more kinds of flowering trees that survive temperatures down to 20 degrees than perhaps any other part of the world.

Fifty years ago the real estate promoters in Southern California were capitalizing on Australia's experience and bringing many of these pretty trees to this country. They succeeded in establishing several hundred kinds of Australian plants on our West Coast, and more recently some of the better ornamentals have been introduced to Florida also.

We have a choice: We can sit back and be content with the few cold-hardy plants we know about, or we can get acquainted with a host of new ones, well worth some strenuous efforts to establish as ornamentals.

The purpose of this is to picture and depict some of the superior flowering trees that ought to get established in Florida. After you have been introduced to these possibilities, your job then is to get seeds or plants and grow them.

Who said it was easy? Nobody will do the job for you; all the initiative must come from the people who live in Central Florida. Now that you are acquainted with some fine new trees worthy of special effort, go get them!

The author was driving through Georgia one sunny May morning when he was suddenly arrested by the sight of a 30-foot tree in front of a Negro's roadside cabin, simply covered with beautiful blue flowers in among the leaves. It was a magnificent sight! Inquiry of the man sitting quietly under the tree, soon solved the question of the tree's identity.

Actually, that beautiful tree was a Princess tree sometimes called "Royal Paulownia," because its scientific name *Paulownia tomentosa* honors Anna Paulowna, ill-fated daughter of the emperor of Russia. It is a Chinese tree and is so cold resistant that an 80-year-old specimen stands in New York City.

It makes its buds in autumn, and starts opening them in spring a little ahead of the leaves, producing great quantities of foxglove-like, reddish purple

43. CALODENDRON CAPENSE (Cape Chestnut)

44. PAULOWNIA TOMENTOSA

flowers that make one think of a Jacaranda, although the trees are not related.

Paulownia trees have gone wild in many places in the eastern United States. Near Tryon, N.C., the highways are lined with them outside the city.

Several kinds of Paulownia trees are in cultivation. The one called *Paulownia fortunei* is much showier in blossom than the other tree, its individual flowers are much larger than those of a Jacaranda. Efforts should be made to grow this particular tree in the Orlando and Central Florida area.

One of the most spectacular of flowering trees is the Boerboom—or literally "Farmer's Bean" which is what the South African Dutchmen call it. The scientific name is *Schotia brachypetala*. The flowers in spring somewhat resemble fuchsia blossoms turned inside out; their intense claret-red color is emphasized because the calyces and flower stalks turn red too, and the flower structure is unusual in another respect—the blossoms arise almost entirely from the woody stems rather than in the leaf axils.

Another common name for this in South Africa is "tree fuchsia" which is unfortunate because that is also the common name of an entirely different tree, *Halleria lucida.*

Schotia is practically evergreen. It is slow growing and for that reason you will never find it in a nursery that seeks to make a quick buck.

There is a 40-year-old tree on the Blossom estate in Palm Beach, which bears a little seed every summer. Here and there over Florida are younger specimens, a few coming into flower, but the tree is rare, and believe it or not, it is extremely rare in cultivation, also in its native South Africa, though it is often found in the wild.

Modern gardeners are in such a big hurry they cannot wait for *Schotia.* The tree is occasionally seen in Southern California because the heavy nectar secreted by the flowers is a rage for the birds.

Another for magnificent display is the Mu Oil tree from China. Its botanical name is *Aleurites montana* and it is a brother of the tung oil tree, *A. fordii,* that thrives up North Florida way.

The accompanying illustration of the Mu Oil tree was photographed in Miami but the trees are common around Gainesville, where the horticultural experts connected with the experiment stations, have made a business of growing the trees for ornament.

As far afield as Hong Kong, these trees are planted by the thousands by the forest department of that British colony, and one of the spectacular sights of spring in that city is the blooming of the Mu Oil trees.

The male and female flowers both of them white, are on different trees. In case you try to grow this from seed, you must put the seed in a plastic bag and store in your refrigerator for a month to let it "ripen." Then when planted, it will germinate readily.

The southern hemisphere contributes three very pretty flowering trees for today's display, all native to regions where temperatures often go down to 20 degrees. So they should be tough enough to get established in Central Florida.

73

46. ARBUTUS MENZIESII (Madrone)

45. SOPHORA TETRAPTERA

Over in the southwest of England, two Chilean trees have found great favor with gardeners, and they are cultivated under the generalized name of "flowering myrtles." However, they are quite different, they flower at different seasons, and both are worth a special effort to grow here. The names of these "flowering myrtles" are *Myrtus luma* and *Myrtus lechleriana*.

The latter is a very bushy plant to 30 feet, holding its foliage to the ground. It blooms very profusely in the spring, the creamy-white fuzzy blossoms like a Spirea, and flush into coral red when the petals and stamens fall. The berries are scarlet at first, then turn black.

After the flowering the shining young shoots color the bush a golden-copper so that it then competes in foliage with such shrubs as *Vaccinium Ovatum*.

The other "flowering myrtle" is very similar, though it does not hold its foliage to the ground; its flowers are a little larger. These two plants are not presently available in the nursery trade in Florida, but they ought to be, so let's get after the nurserymen to make these splendid ornamentals available to growers here.

Both seeds and plants can be obtained easily in England; the author has brought them in when he was running a nursery and they do well in Florida.

Another Australian is the Moreton Bay chestnut, known scientifically as *Castanospermum australe*. It comes from the south coast of that continent where wintry blasts off the South Polar regions make winter living tough at times, but this tree has proved its resistance.

In fact several large specimens of this tree are growing today in the Orlando area, most of them propagated by seed from the giant specimen that for years stood in the old M. T. Daetwyler nursery in the south part of the city.

This tree is not a chestnut at all. It got that name because the big seeds do look a little like shelled chestnuts and the early settlers of Australia tried roasting and eating them although the taste was anything but good.

Actually the tree belongs to the bean family, and that fact is readily perceived when flowering time comes in the spring, for the blossoms are shaped like sweet peas. They start out to be yellow, but their color changes to orange or reddish as they develop, so that the tree displays sort of a rainbow of color.

The blossoms appear not only among the leaves but often develop directly from the old wood, including a few from the trunk itself. The Moreton Bay Chestnut eventually gets to be a good big tree, so if it is planted on a 50-foot lot, it may cause the owner some trouble later on.

Give it plenty of room to develop.

A tree from Australia's southeast and most heavily populated areas is called by the people there "native frangipani," an unfortunate nickname because the tree is no kin to the frangipani trees grown in Florida and Hawaii (*Plumeria sp.*)

47. SCHOTIA BRACHYPETALA

48. CASTANOSPERMUM AUSTRALE (Moreton Bay Chestnut)

A much better name for the Australian is "wing seed tree" because its seeds have a tail or wing, much like our box elder, except that these seeds come packed in layers in flattened 2-inch pod. The scientific name of the tree is *Hymenosporum flavum*.

Although in the wild rain forest it may reach 60 feet in height and develop a trunk a foot in diameter, in cultivation it is always a small tree, rarely 20 feet. Hence it is grown in many lands as a flowering tree in small gardens.

It is a rapid grower, often flowering in one year from seed. The leaves are evergreen but the tree offers little shade, as its main stem is thin and very upright. The individual flowers are 1-inch bright yellow tubes that fade to cream as they age; they are highly conspicuous as they hang in clusters along the branches and they are sweetly scented.

Another subject with magnificent flowers is the red lily tree or lantern tree (*Tricuspidaria lanceolata*), an evergreen from southern Chile. It has been cultivated in Ireland and England for a century, but so far has never become established in the United States.

A writer in the "Gardeners Chronicle" (London) called it "one of the most meritorious and vividly conspicuous shrubs ever introduced into these islands."

In its native land it becomes a tree to 20 feet, with dark evergreen foliage.

The same writer continued: "The flowers, which are about the size of walnuts, are urn-shaped and of a very brilliant deep crimson color. Borne singly on six-inch stems, the flowers are so numerous on mature specimens that the bushes resemble a bewildering assemblage of quaint, miniature glowing lanterns—a truly amazing and unforgettable sight. The species requires a semi-shaded position and lime-free soil enriched by leaf-mold."

Growers in Central Florida should make special effort to grow two kinds of *Lavatera*, commonly called Tree Mallow. One of these is native to the islands off the southern California coast. It is a shrub or tree to 15 feet; it blooms the first year from seed, its hibiscus-like flowers bright purple. The scientific name of this one is *Lavatera assurgentiflora*.

The other one is a biennial with annual flowering branches, making a tree-like shrub three to 10 feet high and bearing particularly handsome purple-red flowers in great abundance, usually in leafy clusters.

This native to the beaches of the French Riviera is already in limited cultivation in the United States, but here in Florida we have been slow to get acquainted with its possibilities as an ornamental. The scientific name for this one is *Lavatera arborea*.

Blue-flowered trees are so unusual they always attract attention. The Texas mountain laurel (*Sophora secundiflora*) is no exception. It is somewhat tougher than the beautiful Jacarandas that were so badly hit by the cold weather of a year ago. They are somewhat slower growing, but this blue-flowered tree from the Rio Grande is one that all Florida gardeners ought to try to establish in their yards.

Both plants and seeds are available in Florida. Al T. Coith, former park superintendent of Orlando, made an effort to get some of them started in city parks and you can do likewise with a little effort.

This small tree grows to 20 feet, is no kin to the mountain laurel that grows in the Carolina mountains and on northward. In fact it is in the bean family and its flowers will make you think of wisteria when it comes into bloom which it will do as a four-foot tree.

They are a deep, rich bluish purple, very pretty, and the tree is about right for a small yard. It really is native of the Rio Grande region and is commonly cultivated in Texas gardens. We have native *Sophora* shrubs and trees here in Florida but they are yellow-flowered and not particularly pretty. This invader from Texas is much superior.

The Cape chestnut (*Calondendron capense*) is not a chestnut at all, nor related to it. It belongs in the citrus family.

Coming from the Cape of Good Hope, it is regarded by many as one of the most beautiful trees ever introduced from that part of the world. A good many of these were planted in California 50 years ago and they may be found all over the lower end of the state, but relatively few of them have been grown so far in Florida. They will do as well here as other citrus relatives do.

The Cape chestnut is a fairly large tree, often growing to 40 feet but spreading very little. At flowering time it covers itself with festoons of lavender-pinkish flowers that superficially make the tree look like a queen's crape myrtle, though of course the trees are not related.

The name "chestnut" derives from the seeds because they do look a little like the hulled chestnuts you buy in the grocery store, but they are not edible.

49. LUEHEA CANDIDA

Delonix—The Royal Poinciana
Which Really Isn't a Poinciana At All!

The glory of our Florida landscape in May and June, and one of the joys of creation, is the thirty to fifty foot, umbrella-topped tree that we insist on calling the royal poinciana, although it actually does not belong to that genus. But if a rose by any other name would smell as sweet, then the only thing that counts with this native of Madagascar is the cloud of gorgeous crimson or scarlet flowers that swathe its massive top for weeks through the early summer.

Festivals mark the blooming. Housewives cherish the individual blossoms for table bouquets and whole communities preen themselves when a giant royal poinciana, well placed against a solid dark green background of *Casuarina* or mango trees, bursts forth in such elegance and profusion as to stop passing automobile traffic—and that often happens in Florida.

The botanical name for the royal poinciana is *Delonix regia,* and despite our wishes in Florida, the accepted common name for the tree through most of the tropics is flamboyant tree. Since discovery of the tree a century ago by Bojer, it has spread to every frost-free area of the globe. In India it is called peacock flower, flame tree or *Guli-Mohur,* which adds color confusion because that means "flower of gold" in reference to an Indian gold coin. Lancaster explains that the tree is "wrongly" called the "gold mohur" and continues: "The original vernacular name for this tree was *Gul Mohr,* peacock's tail, but it became anglicized to mean the golden coin. No amount of argument will correct the error, so Gold Mohur must this tree be known to the end of the chapter." In Malaya, the tree is called "Flame-of-the-Forest," which confuses it with the related red-flowered, Indian *Butea frondosa.*

There are, botanically, *Poinciana* trees but they are smaller in stature, and the leaves, flowers and seed pods are much smaller; they are strictly tropical American, and technical distinctions separate them from what we call the royal poinciana.

Delonix is a genus of three species in East Africa, Arabia and parts of India, but *regia,* the royal poinciana, is the most beautiful of them all. The "white gold mohur" (*Delonix elata*) is a pretty, nearly evergreen timber tree that is planted in avenues in Madras. In Kenya, "at commencement of the rains in November, it produces large, very handsome white and yellow flowers having long red stamens." These turn orange as they fade. The tree is cultivated as an ornamental throughout India, where it flowers from August until March and efforts have been made recently to establish it in the United States. If successful in Florida, this tree should bloom during the winter tourist season.

The royal poinciana blossoms individually are five-petalled, shaped somewhat like a Cattleya, measure three to five inches across, and are faintly scented. They come in clusters with the earliest leaves on new shoots after a dormant period, so that the large but graceful flowers thus appear on a pale green feathery background before the crown is heavy with foliage. The erect top petal (called "the standard" by botanists) is up to two inches wide, white or

51. DELONIA REGIA (Royal Poinciana)

50. CAESALPINIA PULCHERRIMA (Dwarf Poinciana)

pale pink streaked with crimson, with a very broad, wavy crimson border, a yellowish center and a reddish stalk that fades yellow. The ten bristly stamens are red, white at the base. The other four petals are scarlet, one and a half inches wide, definitely clawed.

There is marked variation in the flower color on different trees, from crimson and scarlet to orange. A primrose-yellow has been reported from Africa. Neal in her book, *In Gardens of Hawaii*, observes that the crimson flowers have a white spot on "the standard" petal, whereas this spot is yellow on scarlet or orange flowers. Whether these color differences are varieties or whether they are brought about by soil conditions which may be changed at will, remains to be proved. The personal correspondence of Capt. Ross Parker, U. S. N. (ret.) reveals that the natives in New Caledonia are reported to alter the color of the flowers by additions of pigments to the soil.

The individual flowers are not fully open until about 9 a.m. and they last only two days. The "standard" curls up and fades on the evening of the first day.

The blooming period in Florida is rarely as early as April or as late as September. In Hawaii, the flowers can be seen for about nine months, from January to September but are at their best in June and July. According to Corner's *Wayside Trees of Malaya*, the seasons are not marked enough in Malaya to induce gregarious flowering, and so every royal poinciana tree follows its own rhythm of leaf change and flowering at intervals of seven to ten months. An avenue in Malaya, therefore, has trees blooming at different times throughout the year and there is no month when some trees are not in bloom.

During cold winters in Florida, the royal poinciana trees are virtually bare of leaves for two months. Then they have a tendency to be ugly because the two-foot, flat, black seed pods hang on and the tree has the faculty during this period of pruning itself, killing and dropping whole branches that clutter the trunk or fail to conform to the umbrella-shaped crown. But if pods and shed branches are kept removed, the tree is not unsightly, grass will grow under it with persistent effort, and the effect is desirable in a large garden or park. Unfortunately, too many persons try to grow the royal poinciana in small yards with disastrous effects. Despite the great span of the crown, the roots are strong enough to prevent the tree being blown over in hurricanes; it just sheds its leaves and lets the wind whistle.

The royal poinciana is fast growing, in good soil sometimes reaching twenty-five feet in four years. But it grows in almost any well-drained soil and does particularly well near the sea. It will not tolerate shade from other trees. It can be grown from cuttings and this method or grafting should produce more satisfactory flowering results than are frequently obtained from seedlings. Occasionally, seedlings fail to bloom for ten years.

The enthusiasm for the royal poinciana, which residents of all tropical areas feel, is very well expressed by Ida Colthurst:

"The leaves with eight to twenty pinnae are handsome in themselves, but drop away during the cold season, and for some weeks after this shedding the trees are extremely unsightly; then, Cinderella-like they almost spontaneously burst into gorgeous scarlet and vermilion masses, bizarre fountains of flame, tossing their laden branches in every direction and best described by their

81

52. COLVILLEA RACEMOSA

53. DELONIX REGIA

French name *Flamboyante*. An avenue of *Gul Mohur,* all in bloom together, is wonderfully effective, but glows too hotly in the intense glare and proves fatiguing to the eye; so much so that one wonders, who indeed, living where they prevail

> Would choose however dear
> That spring should revel all the year?"

"Even planted singly against the blue of the sky, and toned down by the green of surrounding trees, they appear to me as the very embodiment of the spirit of the East, beautiful but wild-looking and seductive!"

One other tree should be mentioned in connection with the royal poinciana, because of their superficial resemblance and close relationship. This is colvillea (*Colvillea racemosa*), also native of Madagascar and sparingly planted in Florida. It would be more widely cultivated except for its failure to produce seeds most of the time. Colvillea flowers which come in October or November, also are red, but there is less profusion and they are set differently, hanging in cylindrical clusters a foot or more long, and the effect above the bright green feathery foliage is magnificent.

There is one colvillea tree in Stuart, Florida, on Riverside Parkway in St. Lucie Estates. There is a big tree on the Blossom estate in Palm Beach, and there was another large one at the old Dicken Nursery near Lake Worth, but it was destroyed by a 1950 hurricane. A tree at Dr. David Fairchild's home in Coconut Grove, another in the Fairchild Tropical Garden, one at 2862 Fairgreen Drive, Miami Beach, and a few trees in Fort Myers, but, unfortunately, these are about all that have been established in Florida. Perhaps the future will find this beautiful tree more widespread.

54. COCHLOSPERMUM VITIFOLIUM (Yellow Silk Cotton)

55. COCHLOSPERMUM VITIFOLIUM

Cochlospermum*

* From the Greek: kochlos—a shell, snail; sperma—seed.

Showiest of Spring-flowering shrubs or trees in South Florida gardens are the *Cochlospermum*, whose brilliant yellow 4-inch blossoms, not unlike Dainty Bess roses, come in many-flowered clusters that continue to open over a period of several months—usually from January 10 to April 15.

The common name—if there is one—is a literal translation of the scientific label for the genus, SHELLSEED,[1] which in turn arises from the fact that the seed, about ¼ inch across, resembles a tiny cockle shell. The ineptness of this name when used to refer to a beautiful golden blossom, is perhaps responsible for the persistence of the royal-sounding old generic name MAXIMILIANEA. This was abandoned by botanists because of its confusing similarity to a genus of palms (*Maximiliana*). But if a rose by any other name would smell as sweet, *Cochlospermum* by the same token would continue to be the loveliest of garden ornaments. The more-appealing Indian common name for a related species, YELLOW SILK-COTTON, derives from the fact that, like its distant kin, the RED SILK-COTTON (*Bombax malabaricum*), the *Cochlospermum* has its seeds imbedded in a mass of silky fibers resembling kapok.

The species most frequently seen in South Florida is the Mexican or Central American *C. vitifolium* (grape-leaved), a tree to 35 feet which begins flowering at 2 feet.[2] The plant is always stiff, rather sparsely branched, and the stout branchlets usually carry the 5–7 lobed leaves only toward their tips. These leaves, 6–8 inches wide, bear a striking resemblance to those of the northern sycamore maple (*Acer pseudoplatanus*).

Cochlospermum is leafless ordinarily from January to May, though the first blossoms have appeared before the foliage is gone. Standley[3] calls it "one of the most showy of Mexican plants. . . . Usually quite leafless when they flower, they are one great mass of showy-yellow blossoms." The densely tomentose, occasional seed pods, the size and shape of a hen egg, form in May and are beginning to burst open as the new leaves come out in June.

Two additional *Cochlospermum* are just beginning to make themselves known in Florida. Most arresting of these is the double-flowered form of *C. vitifolium*. Apparently this developed in Puerto Rico where it is commoner than the single, but because it sets no seed and can be propagated only by cuttings, its distribution thus far has been very limited, and it is not referred to in the horticultural literature of any other locality.[4] It does occur rarely in Cuba where the colloquial name "Fool sticks" refers to the grotesque appearance of the blooming tree with stiff branches sticking every direction with clusters of posies on the tips. The blossoms of the double-flowered form are larger than the single, often 5 inches or more across, and look very much like a spectacular, butter-yellow double peony.

The other *Cochlospermum* gaining favor in Florida is the Indian species, *C. gossypium*, which has flowers almost exactly like *C. vitifolium*, except that

1. Kelsey-Dayton: Standardized Plant Names.
2. Popenoe, description to USDA in 1917 from Guatemala.
3. Standley: Trees and Shrubs of Mexico.
4. Holdridge: Trees of Puerto Rico.

Feb. 29 - 50

Dear Menninger

Why don't you go into the hybridization of Cochlospermum vitifolium — graced the species there are and invites them up. I saw a new form on the road to "Rancho Grande" when we went up to that superb spot with dear old man Henri Pittier in Venezuela last year. I'm returning the superb photographs

As ever yours
David Fairchild

56. COCHLOSPERMUM VITIFOLIUM

57. EVEN THE RED FORM FROM AUSTRALIA?

there are more of them on the plants. In both species the petals (RHS color chart) are Buttercup Yellow 5/1, the anthers Orange Buff 5o7, the hundred or more stamens Apricot 6o9. The perceptible distinctions between the trees are:

	C. vitifolium	C. gossypium
Bark	Red brown	Ash gray
Leaves	Wither brown	Wither brilliant orange
Stamens	———	Trace of Scarlet 19 at base
Sepals	Yellow, like flower. Standard and 2 lower sepals measure ¾ x 1¼". 2 side sepals ⅝ x ¾"	Reddish ¾ x 5⁄16" ¾ x ½"
Peduncle	Yellow	Magenta 27
Seed pod	Hen egg	Goose egg
Seed	¼" across	3⁄16" across

Several authorities[5,6] report that the sepals of both species shed when the flower buds open but this characteristic has not been observed on trees in Florida. In India C. gossypium is characteristic of dry hilly country, occupying the hottest and stoniest slopes.[7] In Florida both species grow readily in sandy or rocky soil without attention after once established. No pests have appeared.

Cochlospermum are strictly tropical in origin and have no close relatives in the Temperate Zone. They are a monotypic genus of the natural order *Cochlospermaceae*, lying between *Bixaceae*, and *Flacourtiaceae*, in both of which they have been included by various botanists in times past. There are apparently[8] 12 species of *Cochlospermum*, 5 in Latin America, 4 in Australasia, 1 in India, 2 in Africa. All are characterized by bright yellow flowers except the Queensland *C. heteronemum* whose bright yellow blossoms are so streaked with purple they are sometimes called "Tiger Flower."[9] Brazil's *C. orinocense*, blooming in October, is "remarkable for its ornamental qualities . . . and beautiful golden florescence."[10] Peru's *C. williamsi* is reported "a magnificent tree."[11] *C. balicum* from the East Indies, has "large, handsome bright yellow flowers" but "the leaves are subject to insect attacks and have a dilapidated appearance."[12] Hawaii's *C. hibiscoides* is probably identical with *C. vitifolium*[13] although the two were separated by Rock. Hawaiians refer to the plants indiscriminately as "Buttercup Tree."[14] The Australian species *C. gillivraei* and *C. gregori* have recently been introduced into Florida but are still in the experimental stage.

5. Bailey: Standard Cyclopedia of Horticulture.
6. Blatter & Millard: "Some Beautiful Indian Trees."
7. Brandis: Indian Trees.
8. Bailey: Flora of Queensland.
9. Audas: Australian Trees.
10. "Album Floristico," published by Brazil Agric. Dept.
11. Macbride: "Flora of Peru."
12. Rock: Ornamental Trees of Hawaii.
13. R. A. Young, USDA, correspondence with the author.
14. Neal: In Gardens of Hawaii.

58. CHORISIA SPECIOSA — Type I-A

59. CHORISIA SPECIOSA — Type I-A

The Confusing Chorisia Trees

From Florida to Texas to California and elsewhere in warm regions throughout the world is cultivated a Brazilian ornamental flowering tree that blossoms usually from October to December. Despite its spectacular beauty it is comparatively rare because it is much too large for most yards. In this country it rarely sets seed, and it does not propagate readily by other means. But the amazing thing, which upsets all the textbook foundations, is that no two of these trees are exactly alike.

Scientifically the tree is known as *Chorisia speciosa* St. Hil., but that is just a name. Every owner of a *Chorisia* tree is sure that his is the real *"speciosa,"* and the entirely different tree in the neighbor's parkway must be something else. But until some taxonomist sits down and starts all over again on this genus at the beginning, both these trees and many others equally dissimilar are going to be *"speciosa"* which, fittingly, means beautiful. All *Chorisia* trees described in this article belong to the *"speciosa"* group with this exception: There are a very few *Chorisia* trees in the United States that have yellow flowers and are not beautiful. They are an Argentine immigrant named *C. insignis* and are described near the end of this article.

Florida parks and gardens boast a good many *Chorisia* trees, but the largest of them all, and one of the most beautiful, is on the Coachman place near Clearwater. It is probably 50 years old, stands more than 50 feet high and is as much across the crown. Here indeed is a bouquet for a giant. But the flowers of this tree are so different, not only in color, but in shape, size, formation and general appearance, from the flowers of other *Chorisia* trees, that the author undertook to determine which was which. Consulting reference books only increased the confusion; not enough authors had ever seen more than one *Chorisia* tree. The first definite progress was made when photographs of three quite different *Chorisia* blossoms were submitted to the New York Botanical Garden for helpful comment. These photographs are reproduced in connection with this article. Mr. Joseph V. Monachino of the Garden staff offered these observations:

"The three photographs look like those of three structurally different flowers, the Swinglehurst tree and the Christian Science Church tree of a similar type, although not identical, and the Montgomery estate tree of a much different kind.

"The flowers of the specimens filed in our herbarium under *C. speciosa* also display marked divergencies. Your specimens could be placed here if the variation is accepted to be of a single species. However, the identity of some of our material is questioned, and the group appears to be in confusion. The deeply split filament tube of the pink-purple flower (Swinglehurst tree) suggests *Ceiba* rather than *Chorisia*, but the filament tube of the pink flower (Christian Science Church tree) is also partly split. The size, shape and color of the petals also seem to vary.

"The photograph of the Swinglehurst tree you sent resembles the photo-

60. CHORISIA SPECIOSA — Type I-B

61. CHORISIA SPECIOSA — Type II

graph of *Chorisia pubiflora* appearing on Plate 1 of Dawson's article (G. Dawson: 'Las especies del genero Chorisia cultivadas para adorno en la republica Argentina.' *Revista Argentina de Agronomia* 2:1-10. 1944), but the petals look narrower, their margins are more wavy and the stamens are more erect. The united staminal tube shown in your photo of the Montgomery estate tree is as it should be in *C. speciosa*, according to description. The flower of the Christian Science Church tree is not in complete agreement with either of the other two but is closer to the Swinglehurst tree. This divergence does not, however, necessarily prove specific differences. What it does indicate, I do not know.

"Dawson suggests that *C. pubiflora* is very close to *C. speciosa* and may possibly be a case of mutation.

"The group must be carefully studied or revised to permit any conclusion, in my opinion. This would necessitate better herbarium material than what we now have. Not in a position to borrow specimens from other herbaria and do special study in *Chorisia* myself, I scouted around to see whether any one else would care to work with the genus. Neither my colleagues, nor the visiting botanists I have spoken to, care for the job at the present time.

"You have previously sent individual flowers, and now the three photos. If you will collect for us, good herbarium material of the three trees, that is, complete specimens, attached flowers and leafy branchlets ample enough to fairly cover a 15.5 by 11.5 inch sheet, this material could be deposited in our herbarium. It will constitute a permanent record of the problem we have encountered, and may help suggest to some botanist revisionary studies with the genus. Then, there will be some return, at least for the time and effort I and others who have attempted to aid us, have devoted to the subject."

Growing out of this correspondence, the author has spent two years collecting information and photographs of *Chorisia* trees in various parts of the world, and these are here presented as the basis of a better general understanding of the genus, and a more detailed study of its peculiarities in the future.

The author has arbitrarily separated *Chorisia* trees by the flowers into "showy, white lily, and pink lily" types which correspond to the Montgomery, Christian Science Church and Swinglehurst trees discussed by Mr. Monachino, in that order. Also presented is the "purple *Chorisia*." Because none of these four corresponds with any degree of accuracy with K. Schumann's illustration of *C. speciosa* in the original study of the species, that artist's conception is also reproduced.

In the descriptive matter which follows, emphasis is placed primarily on the differences encountered, because it is these which are the cause of the existing widespread confusion.

Chorisia speciosa St. Hil., sometimes called the FLOSS-SILK TREE, is indigenous to Brazil and the Misiones region in Argentina, and is widely cultivated in both countries. Its spectacular crimson or pink or white five-petaled flowers are bigger, the palmate leaves are larger, and the trunk is fatter than in other species of *Chorisia*. Most trunks are heavily studded with stout, sharp thorns as the accompanying illustration indicates; these may disappear with

62. CHORISIA SPECIOSA – Type II

63. CHORISIA SPECIOSA – Type II

age, Hoehne says, in some trees; in others they are entirely absent from the start. Among the hundred or more *Chorisia* trees the author has seen the only completely thornless specimen is in the Goodwin Memorial Park at Fort Pierce, Florida. It was severely damaged in the August 1949 hurricane but is recovering.

There is a wide variation in the color, size, shape and arrangement of the flowers. Note the confusion of color among these authorities:

Engler & Prantl: "Flowers are red violet, on yellow background with dark streaks."

Britton: Puerto Rico: "Flowers violet red."

Bailey's *Hortus Second:* "Flowers yellowish, striped with brown at base."

Jose Augustin Maldonado, University of Tucumán, Argentina. "The flowers are crimson, but there are wide variations in the rosy color of the petals, and in the flutings at the base of the flower."

Dr. Teodoro Meyer, University of Tucumán: "Rosy flowers."

Michael Grabham in *"Flowers Seen in Madeira,"* p. 51: "Petals oblong, all shades of purple, brown spotted at the base."

G. E. Maul, Museu Municipal do Funchal, Madeira: "Colors vary from very pale mauve, almost creamy-white, to fairly dark purplish-red with yellowish inner halves."

Observer in India: "Deep pink with yellowish and brown stripes at the base."

Observer in Texas: "Dark rose pink turning to white at the base."

Observer in California: "Flowers are pink, brown and yellow."

The flowers were described by Karl Schumann, in *Martius. Fl. Bras.* 12^3: 206-207. 1886, as follows:

CALYX campanulate, 1.5-2 cm. long, glabrous outside, 3-5 lobes.

PETALS 4 or 5 times as long as calyx, 7-9 x 2.2-3 cm., obovate-spatulate, undulate in lower part, white-tomentose outside, violet or red inside, and near base punctate and striped with black, emarginate.

STAMEN TUBE almost equalling petals, 7-8.5 cm. long, yellow; staminodia 5-7 mm. long.

One specimen in the herbarium of the New York Botanical Garden is marked: "Deep rose pink, basal part white, blotched with narrow oblong purple spots."

In an effort to separate these confused descriptions into general types, the author suggests this preliminary outline:

SHOWY CHORISIA: TYPE I—All those with backward flaring, bright pink petals.
  (a) staminal column white; crown dark, drooping, solid.
  (b) staminal column colored, crown white, split, flared, not drooping.
  (c) staminal column colored, petals not overlapping.

WHITE LILY CHORISIA: TYPE II—Petals tipped forward, white or shell pink with pink or red markings; filaments partly split.

PINK LILY CHORISIA: TYPE III—Like Type II except filaments split halfway down, petals narrower and more pointed, bright pink on outer half.

PURPLE CHORISIA: TYPE IV—Like II and III except filaments are com-

64. CHORISIA SPECIOSA — Type III

65. CHORISIA SPECIOSA

pletely free; ends of petals bright pinkish-purple, streaked. Petals overlap left-handed instead of right.

Probably all the other flowering specimens of *Chorisia* in the United States were introduced by the United States Department of Agriculture through the Plant Introduction Garden at Coconut Grove, Florida; the Plant Introduction Numbers are 88221, 104108, 118374 and 139276.

SHOWY CHORISIA IN INDIA.

At the Forest Research Institute, Botany Department, New Forest (Dehra Dun), U. P., India, the officer in charge, Mr. M. B. Raihade, makes these observations of *Chorisia speciosa* Type I in cultivation there:

Flowers deep pink with yellowish and brown stripes at the base.

Petals long, strap-shaped, narrowed at the base, pubescent on the back.

Petals stand out more or less straight.

Edge of petal may be termed crepy.

Staminal tube united its full length.

Collar at the end of staminal tube white, darkening later; solid.

Style extends beyond the collar about ¾".

Base of trunk thorny, thorns not shed; branches thorny.

SHOWY CHORISIA IN TEXAS.

At the Baker-Potts Nursery, Harlingen, Texas, Mrs. Marie P. Kornegay reports on her *Chorisia speciosa* Type I, as follows:

"We obtained our tree from the U.S.D.A. (originating in Sao Paulo, Brazil), and it has done very well. It reached 20-25′ high and 12-18″ diameter when a very severe cold spell in 1948 cut it half way back. It again reached 25′ and was hit pretty hard by cold in December 1950, when in full bloom. It was frozen to the ground in that storm, but has made good recovery and in September 1952 it was again 15 to 18 feet high. It appears to sustain no lasting damage. It has never set seed. The flowers come in November-December. The flowers are a dark rose pink turning to white at the base, and resemble a single white hibiscus in many respects. I believe there is little or no fragrance."

SHOWY CHORISIA IN MADEIRA. G. E. Maul, Museu Municipal do Funchal,

Madeira, writes as follows:

"Regarding *Chorisia*, this tree is very common here in parks, avenues and private gardens, and the predominant colour of the flowers is a bright pink with a creamy-white inner half of the petals which is mottled with brown. The enclosed photograph is of a representative of the most common type. On the other hand, colors vary from very pale mauve, almost creamy-white, to fairly dark purplish-red with yellowish inner halves. I have never seen a yellow flower. The seeds of one and the same tree may produce any of these aforementioned shades of colours.

"The petals generally stand at a right angle to the pedicel of the flower, but sometimes they reflex and fall back slightly.

"The tree trunks are generally quite straight, only some showing a slight tendency towards a bottle shape during their younger stages. The colour of the trunk is dark brown only in very old and large specimens, otherwise it is bright green. They are always very thorny and sometimes. in large specimens, the main roots become visible above the ground,

67. CHORISIA SPECIOSA.

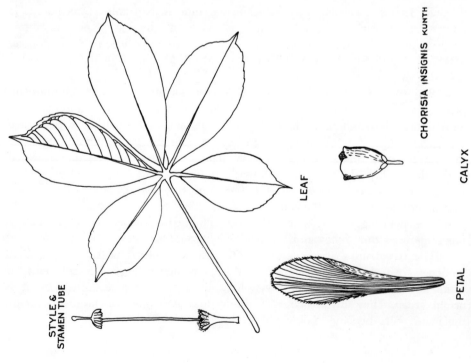

STYLE &
STAMEN TUBE

LEAF

CHORISIA INSIGNIS KUNTH

PETAL

CALYX

66. CHORISIA INSIGNIS

SAMOHU CHORISIA. *Chorisia insignis* H.B.K.

Simplest separation is accomplished by calling these the yellow-flowered *Chorisia* trees. Native of Peru and northeastern Argentina, this species has three recognized forms, differing as the result of ecological conditions under which they grew. Dr. Teodoro Meyer of the Miguel Lillo Institute, in his book, "*The Indigenous Trees Cultivated In The City Of Tucumán*" (1947) says that the cultivated specimens of *C. insignis* in the city of Tucumán, Argentina, are of two distinct forms, one with flowers whose yellow petals have chestnut-colored blotches on them, and the other whose whitish-yellow petals are without spots. An entirely different form is found in the driest parts of Argentina where the tree's appearance is grotesque because the trunk swells enormously in the middle to give a pronounced bottle shape. This misshapen enormity has perhaps given rise to the native name "Drunken stalk." (*Palo borracho*).

This *Chorisia* regardless of the type, would scarcely be classed as an ornamental flowering tree. Its over-fat trunk, sometimes to 6 feet in diameter, with the smooth green bark covered with stout spines or cones, seems too big for the tree, even though it occasionally rises to 50 feet, for the crown is open and rather sprawling. Sometimes the spines disappear as the tree ages.

The color of the flowers depends on which type is being described. Kunth was not describing the same tree as Meyer when he recorded the color of the petals as "pale pink margin, center yellowish." Bailey calls the petals "yellowish striped with brown, about the size of those of flowering dogwood." Sturrock describes the tree at the Harvard garden in Cuba as having "large, open creamy-white flowers."

Genevieve Dawson (*Revista Argentina de Agronomia*, II (1); 1-10. 1944) separates *C. insignis* H.B.K. from the other species cultivated in Argentina by its white flowers. The author notes concerning it "ésta especie, es bien conocida por sus flores blancas o marfilinas." In *Bull. Jard. Bot. Buit.* 3 (6):201 (1924), *C. insignis* is also separated from the other species by its white flowers, "petala alba vel ochroleuca."

In the face of these divergent records of the flower color, be it recorded that the tree at Boynton Beach, Florida, which is pictured with this article, has flowers from July to November that are a beautiful golden yellow, without spots, streaks or marginal improvements. This fades to whitish-yellow, streaked, when the blossoms become quite unattractive; they hang on, and give the tree an untidy appearance. The tree at Delray Beach, Florida, is very similar; the flowers are the same bright yellow. The only readily discernible distinction is that the style on the Boynton Beach blossom extends two inches or more beyond the staminal tube (see illustration); the Delray Beach tree has flowers with the style extended only one half inch. Herbarium material from both of these trees was examined at the New York Botanical Garden and was reported "in size of flower and shape of petals" to match material filed under *C. insignis* in the herbarium there. In view of the fact that on the Florida trees the color of the petals quickly fades in the sun from clear butter yellow to a streaked yellowish-white, is it not understandable that examination of herbarium ma-

69. CHORISIA INSIGNIS

68. CHORISIA SPECIOSA

terial would adduce the conclusion that the flowers were white before they were dried? Neither of these Florida trees has ever set any seed pods and efforts to propagate vegetatively have been unsuccessful.

Botanists' descriptions of *Chorisia insignis* are so widely different as to suggest they were talking about different trees, whereas actually they probably were observing varying types of the same tree. For example, contrast Kunth in H.B.K. Nov. Gen. Sp. 5: 231. 1821, with Karl Schumann in Martius, Fl. Bras. 12³:206. 1886.

	Kunth	*Martius*
Shape of leaflet	obovate-oblong	oblong or obovate-oblong
Apex of leaflet	acuminate	cuspidate
Base of leaflet	cuneate	round or acute
Margin of leaflet	faintly undulate-crenate to-wards apex	revolute, apex serrulate
Petals	spatulate, obtuse, emarginate, silky-tomentose outside, pubescent inside	oblong, obtuse, not undulate. 5-6x1.7 cm. Outside whitish tomentose, inside tomentulose.

There have been several introductions of *Chorisia insignis* into the United States, notably P.I. 42292 and P.I. 82220 by the U.S.D.A., and the author has distributed trees he raised from seed received from Argentina in 1946. Other than the trees at Boynton Beach and Delray Beach, he has no record of flowering specimens in the United States.

OTHER SPECIES OF CHORISIA

In the Index Kewensis, only two other species of *Chorisia* are recognized. One of these is *C. crispiflora* H.B.K. (Syn. *C. ventricosa*), a tree to 75 feet in the coastal area of Brazil. Losing its leaves in February-March, the flowering season, "its large pink flowers make it a very showy tree." Petals are 8-9 cm. long, 11-14 mm. wide. Common names for it in Brazil are "Barriguda" and "Paineira." This species is also reported as introduced to Kenya Colony, Africa, "with large pinkish-red flowers; does well up to 6500 feet." This tree is not in cultivation in the United States.

The other recognized species is *Chorisia soluta* from Guatemala, which is unknown here. And now the confusion is resumed. *C. rosea*, listed in Index Kewensis, probably should be *Ceiba rosea* Seem. K. Sch. One of the collections in the herbarium of the New York Botanical Garden is titled MORONG 1075. This originally was named *Chorisia speciosa* and cited as such in Mor. & Britton's *Enum. Pl. Paraguay*, but it was re-named *Ceiba pubiflora* K. Schum., by Britton & Baker in the *Journal of Botany* 35:176 (1896). Hassler, in B. H. Boise 2 (7):176 (1907) cites the same number as *Ceiba Glaziovii* K. Schum. G. Dawson cites it as *Chorisia pubiflora* (St. Hil) Dawson.

Until some scholar makes a systematic study of the genus *Chorisia*, there will continue to be a wide difference of opinion on which species is which.

70. SUCKERS (female?) AROUND MALE RUPRECHTIA

71. RUPRECHTIA CORIACEA

Sex and My Ruprechtia Tree

For 29 years I was secretary of the Board of Directors of the Martin County Hospital, Stuart, Florida. For many years keeping the door of the institution open was a rugged experience. But in 1940 a benefactor constructed a new hospital building for us with 20 beds and we were inordinately proud of it.

A few years later we undertook to landscape the property which had been given to us and from the nursery I was operating, I donated a dozen or more ornamental flowering trees.

One of these was planted near the front door of the building and it happened to be a Venezuelan tree known botanically as *Ruprechtia coriacea* (Karsh.) Blake. In its native land the vernacular name for the tree is *Biscochito*. Some 20 species of *Ruprechtia* are known in Mexico to South America but this is the only one which has ever been established in the United States. It is a 20 foot evergreen tree, in the same family (Polygonaceae) as buckwheat, rhubarb, and seagrape. *Ruprechtia* trees are dioecious, which means that the flowers of the two sexes are on different trees and it takes two to make a bargain. It is impossible to know whether a seedling tree is a male or a female until it flowers, which means a delay of anywhere from 7 to 15 years.

Of course, I had no idea of the sex of this tree. I had grown several hundred of them from seed obtained in Venezuela and today some are growing on the Sunshine Parkway, a toll road from central Florida to Miami.

The little tree in front of the hospital prospered and grew. Nobody took any special interest in it until Christmas 1958 when it burst forth with quantities of beautiful red flowers. This was a first announcement that the tree was a female because the female flowers on *Ruprechtia* are beautiful, a brilliant red and produced abundantly. Contrariwise, the male flowers on *Ruprechtia* are tiny, red, so inconspicuous that one must approach close to the tree to even see them. All were happy that the hospital tree was a female and every Christmas it produced lots of lovely red flowers.

Many persons approached me on the street and asked: "Have you seen that beautiful red-flowered tree up at the hospital?" Usually I would answer: "Yes, I grew it from seed."

The flowering of the *Ruprechtia* tree was an annual event because in bloom it is very conspicuous. Female flowers look a lot like the samaras on a box-elder tree produced in great quantities; they are at first yellowish green but as the sun strikes them they turn an intense brilliant red and hang on for a month or more.

This was the situation until 1962 when the hospital directors decided to build a new and bigger hospital to accommodate the increasing load of patients. About this time I left the Board of Directors. When the contract for the new building was let, obviously some of the landscaping in front of the hospital building had to be moved and this included the *Ruprechtia* tree.

73. TRIPLARIS AMERICANA

72. Male flowers of RUPRECHTIA

It had to be placed where it would be out of the way. A nurseryman was called in to move it; he root-pruned it properly, cut it back severely, and at the proper time moved it to a different location in front of an auxiliary building, at one time occupied as a nurses' home. From here on the story must be told chronologically:

Christmas 1962. The new hospital building was being finished but the *Ruprechtia* tree was much as it had been when first replanted. It was still alive with a few leaves on it but it had not begun to recover from the move.

Christmas 1963. The *Ruprechtia* tree had definitely recovered from the move and was growing but not too enthusiastically.

Christmas 1964. I went by to see how our little tree was doing and whether it was going to bloom this year. I drove close to the tree but could not see anything; there was no splash of red. I got out of the car and went over to the tree and discovered that it was covered with tiny red flowers so small they could scarcely be seen. The tree had changed its sex completely. It was full of male flowers! Obviously, the hardships of being cut back, root-pruned and moved had upset the sex regimen in the tree's life and it was embarking on a new career.

I was horrified. I actually worried about this transformation, and tried to get some information from other plantsmen but without much success.

I went back to see the tree again a month later and was startled to find an entirely new development. All around the tree in an area of 100 square feet, a whole forest of suckers or root sprouts had come into being. At least 40 young *Ruprechtia* trees were trying to spring up around the old tree. It had never suckered before. This time I called in my genetics friends and asked them a lot of questions. What they told me in effect was that in all plants both sexes are really present and although this one normally manifested the female dominance, when this got upset the male took over. My informants suggested that the suckers were probably all females protesting violently against the other sex having risen to dominance. This was a possibility that I thought needed exploring, so I employed a nurseryman to go down to the hospital and put layers on each one of these suckers. This was properly done, incisions made in the bark to encourage root formation, a sphagnum moss compress impregnated with rooting compound was packed around each stem and a plastic casing fastened over all. This was in April. The stems had grown vigorously and were an average of an inch in diameter.

I left town for the summer, but when I returned in October, I was astonished to see that the moss compresses were still in place on the suckering trees. Some of them by this time were 6 feet or more high. I felt the nurseryman had neglected them, but on examination I found that no roots had formed. At each place where the nurseryman had put a poultice, a huge callous had developed, many of them as big as Irish baking potatoes, but there were no roots. I got a saw and cut them all off near the ground. I took them to a nursery and we planted these in 5 gallon cans, with appropriate chemicals, hoping this would force them to develop roots from the callouses. The shoots were all cut back to two feet high, all foliage was taken off and they were turned over to the nursery for suitable care. The cuttings all grew, they produced plenty of green foliage, and I thought we were on the road to establishing these plants. However I was too optimistic. One by one they died and we lost all of them. Not a single one of the cuttings became established. Consequently, I will never know whether they were females or males.

Christmas 1965. The "papa" *Ruprechtia* tree was in full foliage and it produced a lot of its insignificant flowers. It was just another tree of no special interest at all.

Christmas 1966. This time I was a patient in the hospital myself and I couldn't see anything, but visitors to my room told me of the beautiful red-flowered tree that was in bloom on the hospital grounds. Did I know about it?

Yes, I knew a lot about it. When they told me it had pretty red flowers, I thought at first that "papa" had surrendered and "mama" had again taken over her domain. Later I discovered that the pretty red flowers my friends had reported were on another tree, a *Ruprechtia* female all right, but one that had never been disturbed. The tree that had switched sex was still a male; there were no suckers; "mama" had given up.

The phenomenon of changing sex in plants is not too uncommon. (A dozen examples are cited in my book *Fantastic Trees,* Viking Press 1967.) But please don't ask me anything about sex in plants. All I can tell you is what I have seen, and I took pictures along the way so you could enjoy this phenomenon too.

Ruprechtia flowers are much like those of *Triplaris* (q.v.). The two trees however are easily distinguished: *Ruprechtia* leaves are 3 inches long, *Triplaris* are 12 inches long or more.

Triplaris

Triplaris is the name chosen 200 years ago by Linnaeus, the "Father of Botany," for a group of South and Central American trees and shrubs. There are about 20 species of which *Triplaris americana* is best known. Although commonly planted in the Panama Canal Zone and elsewhere through Tropical America, the genus is practically unknown in the United States.

Triplaris trees grow ordinarily to 30 feet with a straight trunk but little or no spread. They have rather large, green leaves which, when they first unfold, are a lovely dark wine color and make you think for a moment of our common *Sea-Grape,* which has the same peculiarity and to which *Triplaris* is related.

On *Triplaris,* the male and female flowers are found on separate trees, and the sex cannot be told until blooming time. Ordinarily, the male flowers are rather inconspicuous, but the female blossoms, borne in March in profusion, are great masses of bright purplish red and these last for several weeks if the weather is dry. They make the trees conspicuous at a considerable distance.

The calyx, which is the cup that holds each flower, also turns brilliant red, so whether in flower or fruit, *Triplaris* trees are exceedingly showy and handsome. The calyx is important because it has three winged two-inch blades like a tiny shuttlecock, with the nut-like seed in the center. When finally the fruit is ripe, the whole calyx drops off the tree with its burden. It whirls rapidly with its propeller blades, descends slowly like a parachute, and ordinarily reaches the ground at some distance from the tree.

There are no "common names" for *Triplaris* that you could pronounce easily because the trees are common only among Spanish speaking people. The exception is in British Guiana, where *Triplaris* is called *Long John.* In Salvador it is called *Mulato* from the color of the bark. In Nicaragua it is called *Volador* from the winged seed. In Costa Rica it is called *Hormigo* because hollow branches, in that country, are sometimes inhabited by vicious little ants which swarm down on the woodsmen if they try to cut down the tree for its easily-worked timber. There are at least thirty other "common names" for the tree in other countries. Perhaps it is easier just to learn the correct scientific name—*Triplaris.*

Barro Colorado is the name of an island you pass when you go by boat through the Panama Canal. For many years it has been a rendezvous for scientific men because Harvard University has maintained a laboratory there where they could work. Thomas Barbour was largely responsible for creating that laboratory and in his book, "A Naturalist at Large," he pays glowing tribute to the magnificent flowering trees to be seen in that part of the world. He wrote:

"I don't know whether I shall ever see Barro Colorado again, but I certainly hope that I may, if only to sail by it through the Canal in the month of March, when the Guayacan trees (*Tabebuia guayacan*) lift their lofty heads above the forest top, each as glittering as a golden dome, while the purple Jacarandas, the pale pink Almendros (*Dypteryx panamensis*), and the Palo Santo (*Triplaris americana*) with flowers as crimson as arterial blood make a scene of incomparable splendor."

Barbour did not live to see that day, but here in Florida we are beginning to re-create the beauty he wrote about, for we are already growing Jacaranda and Tabebuia, and now *Triplaris,* whose brilliant color Barbour loved so well.

74. TABEBUIA PALLIDA (Cuban Pink Trumpet)

TABEBUIA—Our Best Yard Trees

The most satisfactory flowering trees for parkway and yard planting in southern Florida belong to the genus *Tabebuia*. This Brazilian native name applies to about 150 species of broad-leaved, mostly evergreen trees from the West Indies and Central and South America. Some of them were formerly included in *Tecoma*,[1] some still are; in this article correct botanical names are retained, but all are lumped together as Tabebuia trees.

Almost without exception they are showy-flowered and precocious, with trumpet-shaped blossoms, white, pink, lavender, purple, red and yellow, frequently in great profusion. F. C. Hoehne, dean of plantsmen in Sao Paulo, Brazil, in his book *City Planting of Trees*, sums up the utility of the *Tabebuia* group when he says: "To name the species most worth cultivating is easier than to exclude those not worth while," and then he suggests ten outstanding kinds for street planting in Brazil; about half of his choices are now growing in Florida too.

Of the dozen or more species under cultivation generally in Florida now, commonest is the Paraguayan silver-trumpet tree (*T. argentea*[2] Britton; Syn. *Tecoma argentea* Bur. & K. Schum.) which owes its common name to the silver-gray cast of its evergreen leaves.

Also commonly cultivated are three species that are much confused, even by botanists. Two quite different trees have been introduced into Florida under the name of *T. Pallida* Miers. One of these, commonly called the Cuban Pink Trumpet, is evergreen and it flowers on and off all year, usually with the ovate-lanceolate leaves but often while leaf change is in process. The deciduous *T. pallida* (sometimes called *T. pallida* No. 2) drops its linear-obcordate leaves (which have an irridescent oily sheen) once a year and while bare, blooms profusely, then puts on its new foliage. Many specimens of both trees are in common cultivation. The third tree, which too is often seen, is *T. pentaphylla* Hemsl., national tree of Salvador, with leaves three times as big as those of either *T. pallida*. Standley says that in Central America this tree "is densely covered with flower panicles so as to form a giant bouquet. . . . an unsurpassed display of color varying from nearly white to deep rose; in their tints the flowers recall the Japanese cherries and are equally beautiful." Bailey's *Hortus Second* confounds the confusion surrounding these three trees by calling them identical.

Other *Tabebuia* trees now commonly planted in Florida, though on a smaller scale because more recently introduced and not so well known, are:

> *T. palmeri* Rose, Bright Pink. Mexico.
>
> *T. guayacan* (Seem.) Hemsley. Yellow. Panama.
>
> *T. rosea* (Bertol.) DC. Pink. Colombia.
>
> *T. serratifolia* (Vahl) Nicholson. Yellow. Trinidad.

[1] Without any apparently valid reason, *Tecoma stans* is referred by *HORTUS SECOND* to *Stenolobium Stans* and therefore is so treated here.

[2] In this article the Abbreviation *T.* stands for *TABEBUIA*.

75. TABEBUIA ARGENTEA (Gold tree or Silver Trumpet) 76. TABEBUIA GUAYACAN

T. chrysantha (Jacq.) Nicholson. Yellow. Colombia.

T. avellanedae (*Tecoma ipe* Mart.) y T. Dugandii. Rose to purple. Northern South America.

Here are seven reasons why these *Tabebuia* trees are termed most satisfactory in Florida:

(1) They produce their floral display in winter or early spring when the tourist population is at its height. *T. palmeri* begins blooming in December and the other species keep up the procession of beauty through May. Although the flowering periods are usually two to three weeks, the evergreen *T. pallida* blooms almost continuously for eight or ten weeks—March to May—and repeats with a shorter period later in the year. Several species flower when only three or four feet high. Most species of *Tabebuia* are evergreen, but even those that drop their leaves do so when flowers are ready to bedeck the limbs, so that the trees are almost never bare, even in winter.

(2) With the exception of *T. donnell-smithii*,[3] all the species being grown in Florida are small enough to find place in the average yard and not to outgrow their location.

(3) No diseases or pests of any kind appear to attack the *Tabebuia* now in cultivation.

(4) The glossy-leaved *Tabebuia* are sufficiently salt-resistant to permit their use in landscaping of waterfront homes. A considerable number of the trees are in successful cultivation around homes in Palm Beach where salt spray from the trade winds over the Gulf Stream is a considerable factor.

(5) Some species of *Tabebuia* withstand inundation for extended periods without damage. At Fort Lauderdale, Fla. in June 1947, specimens of *T. rosea* and *T. pentaphylla* were covered by flood waters for six weeks without injury. *T. aquatilis* (E. Mey.) Sprague & Sandwith of northern Brazil, grows naturally in inundated savannas and reaches a height of 100 feet or more. *T. insignis* (Miq.) Sandw. is indigenous to swampy forests of the Guianas and Venezuela.

(6) Other species are particularly suited to dry regions. *T. leucoxyla* DC. thrives in Trinidad in "very dry and exposed situations," and *T. serratifolia* is a very slow-growing Trinidad forest tree, found only on dry hillsides with gray wood so hard that it weighs 70 pounds per cubic foot. (Compare balsa 7 pounds, cork 13, oak 40, mahogany 45, ebony 73.)

(7) Some species of *Tabebuia* are sufficiently hardy to thrive in central and north Florida. This has long been known to be true of *T. argentea*. In Orlando, Florida mature specimens of *T. umbellata* Sandwith, thrive despite occasional low temperatures of 26° or a little less. This species was brought from Brazil by Mulford Foster, distinguished authority on bromeliads, and is now much used as a street tree by the City of Orlando Parks department. It flowers extravagantly in April. There are a few trees of other species of *Tabebuia* in cultivation experimentally in other parts of northern Florida and

---

[3] Several *Tabebuia* have been transferred to the genus *Cybistax* and three of these are cultivated in Florida. *C. donnell-smithii* F. N. Rose (*Syn. T. donnell-smithii* J. N. Rose) often grows to 100 feet; in Mexico it is called Prima Vera. *C. chrysea* (Blake) Siebert (Syn *T. chrysea* Blake) with lovely yellow flowers, is much used as a street tree in Barranquilla, Colombia. The green-flowered *C. antisyphilitica* Mart. is a strange and beautiful Brazilian tree.

77. TABEBUIA UMBELLATA

78. TABEBUIA SERRATIFOLIA

80. TABEBUIA PENTAPHYLLA

79. TABEBUIA DONNELL-SMITHII

preliminary conclusions are that the deciduous types that grow at high elevations in their native habitats (and therefore are in some measure inured to cold spells during their dormant periods) will probably survive the winter temperatures of all parts of Florida and areas with similar climate.

Because some of the *Tabebuia* provide lumber of exceptional beauty of grain and color, and because others furnish timber of great durability, many of the natural stands of the trees in Central America and elsewhere have been slaughtered. In Salvador at least one species has been saved from extinction only by the organization of the Society for the Beautification of the Highways of Salvador, which has grown many thousands of seedlings and planted them along the roadsides of the nation.

Timber experts, not interested in the ornamental quality of the trees, classify *Tabebuia* on an economic rather than a botanical basis, and recognize three degrees of hardness and durability:

(a) The White Cedar group, in which the wood resembles birch. (*T. insignis, T. aquatalis*).

(b) The Roble group, with brownish, medium hard wood resembling plain sawed oak, not very durable in contact with the ground (*T. pentaphylla.*)

(c) The Lapacho group, embodying a large number of species with olive-brown, more or less oily, very dense timbers containing an abundance of sulphur-like deposits (lapachol compound). The wood is highly resistant to decay. Standley records of *T. guayacan:* "Some of the beams of the cathedral of Old Panama are said to have been of this wood and to have remained sound although exposed to the weather for 250 years." Other important members of this group are *T. avellanedae, T. palmeri, T. serratifolia, T. lapacho* (K. Schum.) Sandwith, *T. barbata* (E. May) Sandwith.

Although it is beyond the scope of this presentation to refer to all known species of *Tabebuia,* attention can be drawn to those offering most promise for ornamental planting in the warmer parts of the United States. The ten Brazilian species selected by Hoehne for street planting are:

T. alba (Cham.) Sandwith—Specific name is from the white fuzzy leaves. Yellow flowers.

Tecoma caraiba. Mart.—A very beautiful tree, with large yellow flowers.

Tecoma chrysotricha Mart.—A beautiful tree of good form and abundant yellow flowers.[4]

T. eximia (Miq.) Sandwith—Dark red flowers.

T. avellanedae—Red, reddish or purple flowers, precocious and ornamental when in bloom.[5]

[4] This tree under the name *Tabebuia chrysotricha* thrives in California. Ray Collett, director of the arboretum at Crown College, University of California, Santa Cruz, writes: "I am not aware of any specimen in Northern California other than our one small tree of *T. chrysotricha.* When I acquired it, I doubted that it would ever bloom here, much less set seed, for the mean temperature of our warmest month is merely 64°. I would not have been surprised if its roots had rotted during our cool, wet winter months. However it has bloomed beautifully each spring. Our tree has never had to endure temperatures below 32°. However there are several trees at the Huntington Gardens, San Marino, California which surely have survived quite low temperatures."

[5] This tree under the name *Tabebuia ipe,* thrives in Stuart, Fla., blooms in February a month ahead of other species, and seeds prolifically.

82. TABEBUIA GLOMERATA

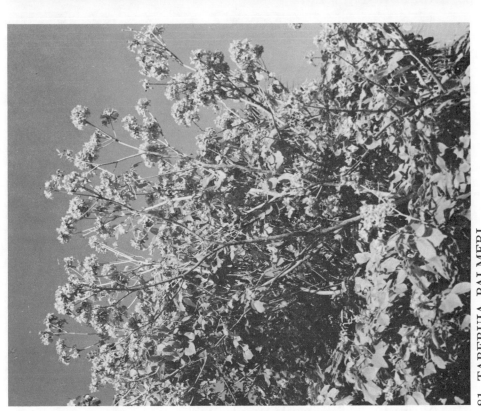

81. TABEBUIA PALMERI

83. TABEBUIA PALMERI

84. TABEBUIA AVELLANADAE (T. IPE)

T. impetiginosa (Mart.) Standley—Large tree of rapid growth. Red flowers.

T. lapacho—Pink flowered. Of most beautiful appearance.

T. leucoxyla—Wonderful in possessing white flowers in great number. (The flowers of the West Indian species are sometimes rosy pink, and in Trinidad the color is described as "pale mauve with yellow throat").

T. ochracea (Cham.)—Very elegant; large yellow flowers.

T. umbellata—Yellow flowers, medium height, slow growth, but easiest of all to transplant.

There are a number of Central American species that are described in glowing terms but which have never been introduced into the United States. These include *T. spectabilis*, of Colombia which is described by Macmillan;[6]

T. aesculifolia Hemsl. described by Rehder as having "orange red flowers with yellow spots on three lower lobes" (this may be confused with *Godmania aesculifolia*, a related tree with greenish-yellow flowers); and *T. stenocalyx* Sprague and Stapf., with large white flowers—one of the few species of Tabebuia with simple leaves; most species have 3, 5 or 7 leaflets.

Other West Indian species which have already been brought into cultivation include:

T. haemantha DC.—Puerto Rican tree with small red or crimson flowers. This has been hybridized with *T. pallida* to produce a tree with large burgundy red flowers.

T. glomerata. Urb.—Puerto Rican tree with clustered bright yellow flowers.

There are at least 50 other species in the West Indies. Britton describes two red-flowered species in Puerto Rico with simple leaves. *T. rigida.* Urb. and *T. schumanniana,* Urb. The Harvard Botanical Garden in Cuba has found special merit in three other West Indian species. *T. heterophylla*, DC. Britton, and *T. lepidota* (H. B. K.) Britton both with pale pink blossoms, and *T. sauvallei* Britton. a shrubby patio type with tiny mauve flowers.

---

[6] Armando Dugan of Colombia, S.A., an authority on the *Tabebuia*, writes. "Of course, *T. spectabilis* (Pl. et Lind. ex. Pl.) Nicholson, which you call Showy Trumpet Tree was originally described from the mountains of northeastern Colombia at 8000 feet, a rather high altitude for *Tabebuia*. The tree reported under *spectabilis* has only been found in Colombia once or twice since it was described in 1887. I have seen no Venezuelan specimens corresponding to the original description."

85. MELALEUCA QUINQUENERVIA (Cajeput)

86. MELALEUCA LINARIIFOLIA

Melaleucas For Florida

Three Australian trees in the past 30 years have transformed the landscape around human habitation in South Florida. They are the Casuarina, commonly called "Australian pine" although not even distantly related to the pines; the Silky Oak (*Grevillea robusta*) which is not an oak at all; the Cajeput which strangely enough is more frequently known by its correct scientific name, *Melaleuca leucadendron*.

Only once before in human history has a landscape been so completely converted—again Australian trees were used for the purpose—and that was 50–60 years ago, when F. Franceschi[1] and T. O. Falkner[2] brought the Eucalypts and the Acacias to a new home in the Golden State.

It is strange that in southern California some 15 species of *Melaleuca* trees and shrubs are commonly cultivated for ornaments while *M. leucadendron* is virtually unknown; while in South Florida *M. leucadendron*[3] is one of the commonest dooryard ornamentals and in some swampy areas around Ft. Myers, Estero, Dania, Stuart and elsewhere the trees have seeded themselves and gone wild, covering considerable areas; yet other species of *Melaleuca* are almost entirely absent.

There are about 100 species of Melaleuca, all shrubs and small trees except a very few larger. All are solely Australian except that varieties of *M. leucadendron* are found in the Philippines and the Malay archipelago. They have bottlebrush-like flowers, white, yellow, pink or purplish, with the stamens in bundles of five. This characteristic distinguishes plants of this genus from their close relatives, the 20 species of Callistemon.

The name Melaleuca is derived from the Greek mela (black) and leukos (white), referring to the old and new bark on some species.

Several times a year this *Melaleuca* covers itself with great masses of honey-

---

[1] Under the inspiration of Franceschi the Southern California Acclimatizing Association was established in 1893, with headquarters at Montecito, later moving to Santa Barbara. Peter Reidel was manager. Mr. Reidel still lives in Santa Barbara, and has completed more than one-half of an encyclopedia of plants introduced in California, more comprehensive and more voluminous than Bailey's. It is hoped that some enterprising publisher will undertake the printing of Reidel's manuscript, as it represents the experience of experts in their introduction of literally thousands of exotic plants. The Association's price list for 1911 describes and offers for sale more than 800 species of rare and interesting plants; its nurseries contained 100,000 plants of more than 1,000 different kinds.

[2] T. O. Falkner, head of the Santa Fe Railroad's lumber division, was alarmed in the early 1900's over the dwindling supply of railroad ties. He persuaded his railroad to buy an old Spanish land grant rancho of 8600 acres near San Diego and plant it to Eucalyptus trees. Falkner went to Australia himself, shipped millions of seeds, and the ranch produced 3,000,000 Eucalyptus trees of many species. When it was discovered that Eucalyptus wood could not be treated successfully for soil rot, the entire project was abandoned. The enormous stand of Eucalypts today beautifies the hills of Rancho Santa Fe, a big home ranch development. See "A Beautiful Mistake" by David Hellyer, in "American Forests," December 1950.

[3] This binomial is retained in Willis's Dictionary (1966) but most botanists now call this tree *M. quinquenervia* (Cav.) S. T. Blake.

88. MELALEUCA QUINQUENERVIA

87. MELALEUCA QUINQUENERVIA

laden flowers, much loved by bees. Unfortunately, the honey they make is of such poor quality that the Central Florida Beekeepers Association is asking that new mass plantings of the tree be discontinued. Cajeput honey is reported to have such a disagreeable odor and flavor that five per cent in mixtures with other honeys lowers the grade to such an extent as to make it unsalable.

Southern California is too cold for this tree. Similarly in Australia, the coastal specimens in Victoria are anything but handsome, whereas in Queensland it is magnificent. Pink and cream-flowered varieties have been reported north of Brisbane.

An outstanding new introduction into South Florida is what the Australians call the Flax-Leaf Paperbark Tree (*M. linariifolia*[4]). The specific name, signifying Linaria-leaved, refers to the genus *Linaria,* or Toad-Flax. A magnificent picture of this spreading, well-shaped *Melaleuca* tree, its top blanketed with a mantle of white flowers, appears in that exceptionally beautiful book, "Melbourne's Garden," with the caption: 'Snow in Summer is the poetic vernacular name given to this famous tree.' (The same picture appears with this article.[5] A. W. Jessup, director of the Melbourne Botanic Gardens, had given me the book and sent seed. The resultant seedlings are being widely distributed through various channels.

C. T. White, beloved director of the Brisbane Botanic Garden, wrote me of this Melaleuca: "The two-inch fluffy flower spikes are white, borne in pairs in great abundance, and rather showy." They are fragrant, too. The tree is only found in the warm coastal areas of New South Wales and Queensland, and because it thrives in swampy places, its wood is valued for piling in wet ground, as well as for turnery and fuel.

The Flax-Leaf Paperbark does have a white, papery bark that peels off in layers. The narrowly-oval one-inch leaves are smooth, often glossy. Distillation of the leaves yields a pale yellow essential oil that has pleasant terpentic and myristic odor.

Most widely planted in Southern California are the Pink Melaleuca (*M. nesophila*), the Prickly Paperbark (*M. styphelioides*), and the Drooping Melaleuca (*M. armillaris*).

"*Melaleuca nesophila* is one of the most beautiful of Australian ornamental trees," wrote E. E. Lord. "It has long been grown and valued in southern California as a park tree, yet in its native land it is rarely seen. It is covered in spring and early summer with numerous mauve-and-gold bottlebrush flowers that make good cuttings." Unlike most *Melaleuca* flowers, these are more ball-shaped and are carried at the branch tips.

Melaleuca styphelioides is another handsome big tree with papery bark,

[4] The specific name is incorrectly spelled *"liniarifolia"* in several reference books. The name was originally published by Smith in Trans. Linn. Soc. London 3:287 (1797) as *"Melaleuca linariifolia,"* and so that is the correct form of the name. There is no reason under the Rules to change its spelling in any way.

[5] In the February 1949 issue of "Parks and Recreation" magazine, there appeared an article by Henry Teuscher, director of the botanical garden at Montreal, Canada, in which he described the beauties of the gardens at Melbourne and the photograph of *Melaleuca linariifolia* was used again in that publication. The author is indebted to Mr. Teuscher and to "Parks and Recreation" for the use of their cut.

89. MELALEUCA ARMILLARIS

90. MELALEUCA NESOPHILA

twenty to sixty feet or more, and someone has called it the ideal street-planting tree, just spreading enough, uniform in growth, and willing to thrive in brackish or boggy soils or anywhere else. It has small, rather prickly, light green leaves, and in spring produces white bottlebrush flowers in great masses.

Melaleuca armillaris ranges from a tall, compact bush to a thirty-foot tree, depending on the wind protection it gets. It likes wet soils, has very fine cut foliage and in spring produces many white, two-inch bottlebrushes.

These three *Melaleuca* trees are grown only sparingly in Florida, where until recently the residents believed only one kind of *Melaleuca* existed—the Cajeput. But growers have now taken strongly to two other, newly-introduced species that hold even greater promise for landscape work. These are the big spreading "Snow in Summer" (*M. linariifolia*), sometimes called Flax-leaf or Narrow-leaf Paperbark, and a more tropical species from northeastern Queensland called "White Cloud" (*M. bracteata,* Syn. *M. genistifolia*).

Melaleuca bracteata is a lovely tall tree to 40 feet or more with hard, blackish, rough bark, quite unlike the paperbarks. The scattered, rigid, acuminate or pungent-pointed, flat, half-inch, dark green leaves, give the tree the appearance of a conifer. But this resemblance vanishes when the copious small white bottlebrush flowers begin appearing all over the branches. They are in oblong spikes, sometimes at the branch tips but usually the axis grows out before the flowers expand, and many of the bracts develop into leaves.

Although the U.S. Department of Agriculture has introduced about fifty kinds of *Melaleuca* trees and shrubs, F. Franceschi grew these and many more, and other experimenters have tried their hands with the genus, but the plants still do not have a wide distribution. The public is almost wholly ignorant of their possibilities, perhaps because none is available in nurseries. None of the shrubs is grown in Florida, although in California the following are cultivated to some extent:

Robin Redbreast (*M. lateritia*). Red flowers. Six to eight feet.
Scarlet Honey Myrtle (*M. fulgens*). Red flowers. Five or six feet.
Crimson Honey Myrtle (*M. wilsoni*). Red flowers. From four to six feet.
Thyme Honey Myrtle (*M. thymifolia*). White flowers. Two or three feet.
Oval-leaf Honey Myrtle (*M. elliptica*). Carmine flowers. Ten feet.
Stiff Honey Myrtle (*M. cordata*). Red flowers. Three feet.
Dotted Melaleuce (*M. hypericifolia*). Red flowers. Eight to ten feet.

91. MELALEUCA BRACTEATA   92. MELALEUCA STYPHELIOIDES

94. BRACHYCHITON POPULNEUM (Kurrajong)

93. BRACHYCHITON ACERIFOLIUS (Flame tree)

Brachychiton Trees from Australia Thrive Here

Trees that grow in Australia have a way of being quite different from trees that grow in other lands, even when they are closely related. Several important groups of useful landscape trees like the Eucalyptus, the Melaleuca, the Callistemon or "Bottlebrush," and the Casuarina (which we carelessly call "Australian pine") are almost exclusively Australian. Most of the "down-under" continent has a very low rainfall, with the result that the vegetation has adapted itself to dry conditions by developing finely cut or very narrow foliage, thus reducing the transpiration and aiding the plant's survival through long periods of drought. Most of the *Acacia* trees are Australian and their exceedingly fine cut foliage is a good example.

In all tropical countries are to be found representatives of a genus of trees called *Sterculia*. (The name is derived from the Latin *stercus*—manure; the flowers of a few species have an offensive odor). There are about 100 different kinds of these trees, but the eleven species found in Australia are so strikingly different from the others, that they were put into a new genus called *Brachychiton*. Several of these are in cultivation in the United States. They make interesting and attractive ornamentals and are worthy of better acquaintance and more widespread use.

Most spectacular in flower is the Flame Bottletree (*B. acerifolius*), better known in Australia as the Illawarra Flame. Waxy, flaming-red, bell-like flowers on red stalks that look like coral, are produced in great masses when the tree is leafless or nearly so, at or near the branch tips, and the pyramidal growth habit of the tree emphasizes the torch effect of the tree in bloom. The exceptionally handsome, palmately-lobed leaves make the stiff, straight tree conspicuous all the year.

Widely planted in southern California, the Flame Bottletree is becoming more and more popular in Florida the past few years since a handsome specimen at the Montgomery place in Coconut Grove began blooming. Because it is a native of New South Wales, the tree is half-hardy and should thrive all over Florida. Ordinarily in cultivation the Flame Bottletree rarely exceeds 20 feet in height, though in the moist, hot conditions of northeast Queensland it reaches 100 feet.

The name "Bottletree" is rather loosely used in connection with the Brachychiton. Some of them do develop a trunk that looks like an oversized milk bottle, particularly *B. australe* and *B. rupestris*, but neither of these have attractive flowers and are not ordinarily cultivated.

The Brachychiton with the biggest and showiest flower is the one the Australians call White Kurrajong or Queensland Lacebark (*B. discolor*), and this is not an uncommon tree now in Florida, a few being planted as a parkway tree in Tampa. It too has very large and handsome, palmately lobed leaves similar to the Flame Bottletree, but it grows much faster, it is tall and more spreading than the other, and its lavender-pink, bell-shaped flowers backed with a thick bronze felt, are about 2 inches long. They are not produced in such

96. BRACHYCHITON RUPESTRIS

95. BRACHYCHITON DISCOLOR

profusion as the red blossoms of the Flame Bottletree, but they are individually much more conspicuous and they cover the ground under the tree with a pink carpet. This tree also will take considerable cold weather, and deserves to be widely planted.

Most popular of the Brachychiton trees in California is the less showy but more adaptable Kurrajong. (*B. populneum*). This used to be called *Sterculia diversifolia,* and the specific name was particularly apt because no trees anywhere have so many different kinds of leaves, often on the same tree—wide or narrow, entire or lobed, round or almost square, so that you can see several trees together and, if not aware of this diversity, be prepared to believe they are quite different trees.

The Kurrajong is particularly prized in Australia because it is highly drought-resistant, its leaves are excellent fodder for cattle where there is no grass, and its attractive, tapering habit provides lots of shade in dry and thirsty areas. The bell-shaped flowers, creamy with chocolate spots, and often with a purple throat, hang in big clusters among the leaves, dainty and pretty. Lord: *Shrubs and Trees for Australia Gardens* calls the flowers "most showy." In time the Kurrajong reaches 50 feet. It is extensively used as a street tree in Southern Europe, and large specimens can be transplanted readily.

Occasionally seen but rare in the United States is a hybrid between the Flame Bottletree and the Kurrajong, with maple-shaped leaves that are wooly on the back side, and clusters of pink flowers while the tree is bare of leaves. In Australia where it reaches 50 feet this hybrid has been found unusually resistant to drought and heat and suitable for street planting and parks.

A Jacaranda without a Name

The 120 genera of Bignoniaceae in tropical America, with some 650 species, provide a host of difficult problems in identification, and many earnest students of the genus have spent lifetimes in puzzlement.

Not the least difficult to understand are the 50 species of *Jacaranda*, only one of which (*J. mimosifolia* D. Don*) is in common cultivation as an ornamental street tree. Its clouds of blue flowers are spectacular sights from Johannesburg, South Africa, to Grafton, New South Wales. This tree is commonly cultivated in southern California, and it thrives in central Florida along a line from Tampa to Melbourne. South of this belt the trees grow well enough but seldom flower until 25–30 years old. Many explanations are offered for this peculiarity; widely held is the belief that nights are too warm in that area and that, to bloom, jacaranda trees (like peaches) require a certain number of cold nights to ripen the flower buds.

Wanting more blue-flowered trees on the South Florida landscape, many nurserymen now are raising seedlings of a dwarf jacaranda tree brought to the United States by this author in 1942 from the forest service nursery at Toledo, Uruguay, under the name *J. Chelonia* Grisebach. The parent tree, now 22 years old, is a street tree in Stuart, Florida, with a rounded crown, and smaller, somewhat darker purple flowers that usually come on 3 or 4 weeks later than the common jacaranda. It is a much more consistent and dependable bloomer than *J. mimosifolia*.

The identity of this jacaranda, however, is still in doubt. In describing *J. Chelonia* ninety years ago, Grisebach** confused and confounded two distinct species, *J. mimosifolia* and *J. cuspidifolia* Kuntze. The result is that *J. Chelonia* Grisebach appears to be a *species falsa*, and the description of it in Bailey's Standard Cyclopedia of Horticulture and other reference works may be disregarded.

Now where does this leave the dwarf tree in Stuart, Florida, which is quite different from the common jacaranda? The author has discussed this matter over a period of years with one of the world's foremost authorities on the Bignoniaceae, Noel Y. Sandwith of the Herbarium, Royal Botanic Gardens, Kew, England, and has supplied him with flowers, foliage, fruits, and photographs of the Stuart tree. Here are excerpts from a sequence of Mr. Sandwith's letters:

"[Concerning] the tree grown by you under the name *Jacaranda chelonia* Griseb. I have long been puzzled over the identity of this taxon, because the sheet with the original material of Grisebach, agreeing with his de-

---

**Jacaranda ovalifolia* R. Brown is a synonym of *J. mimosifolia* D. Don. Many authors cite *J. acutifolia* Humboldt & Bonpland as another synonym, but incorrectly, since this applies to a Peruvian species quite distinct from *J. mimosifolia*. *Jacaranda cuspidifolia* Kuntze is also distinct. (See: Supplement to the Dictionary of Gardening [RHS], p. 250, 1956; and Sandwith in Kew Bulletin 1953; 455–457, Jan. 1954.)

**Goettingen Abhandlungen 19: 223. 1874.

scription, represented here, seems to be a mixture of *J. mimosifolia* (fruit) and *J. cuspidifolia* (flowers). No one recently in Argentina seems to have collected a *tertium quid*, which might be a third species, *chelonia.* . . ."

"The foliage and fruits of your *Jacaranda chelonia* I can match with forms of *J. mimosifolia* here collected in Jujuy and Tucuman. Perhaps the narrow, revolute nature of the leaflets is not constant on all parts of the tree or at all ages and stages? The important point is that your tree is NOT *J. cuspidifolia* . . . I shall be most interested to know what your tree is. . . ."

"The inflorescence of your *Jacaranda* has arrived. There seem to be larger and smaller-flowered forms of very many species of Bignoniaceae and these corollas certainly fall within the range of variation shown on material here. If the smaller, darker corolla is correlated always with precocious flowering, or habit, or shape of leaflets, it may deserve a varietal name under *J. mimosifolia* D. Don. So far as I can see at present it is not correlated with shape of leaflets or any fruit character.

"When I next write to my friend Dr. Humberto A. Fabris, Museo de la Plata, La Plata, Buenos Aires, who specialises in this family, I will call his attention to this matter and ask if he can throw further light on it from the observation of cultivated trees at Tucuman or other Argentine cities, or of native trees in the northeast provinces of Argentina. . . ."

"Dr. Fabris has just written that he recognizes only three species of Jacaranda in his country—*J. mimosifolia*, *J. micrantha* Cham., and *J. semiserrata* Cham. He says he has no Argentine material of *J. cuspidifolia*. . . .

"At present I still regard *J. chelonia* Griseb. as a *species falsa*, compounded of two elements, *J. mimosifolia* and *J. cuspidifolia*, the original element (with fruit) belonging to *J. mimosifolia*, of which *J. chelonia* should be regarded as a synonym. Your tree may, I suppose, be a form or 'race' of the species. Meanwhile, I should not use the name *J. chelonia* for this plant. As I have mentioned, this is a mixture of two distinct species under that name, by its own author.

"A specimen on a second sheet with flowering material (Lorentz & Hieronymus 1175, in Hb. Kew.) which Grisebach passed as *J. chelonia*, does not agree with his other flowering specimen and with his own description of the calyx, and is simply a form of *J. mimosifolia* but with larger flowers (corolla to 4 cm. long) than yours; we have a specimen of it here, with Grisebach's handwriting on the label."

In view of Mr. Sandwith's opinion, the disputed street tree will have to be called "the Stuart jacaranda" until someone comes up with a more specific title. The U. S. Department of Agriculture forty years ago introduced *"Jacaranda Chelonia"* trees and distributed them to experimenters under these numbers: P.I. 63987, 124032, 145605. No effort has been made to run down these introductions or their descendants to determine whether they resemble the Stuart jacaranda.

127

Dr. Russell Seibert, Director of Longwood Gardens, Kennett Square, Pennsylvania, who is the American authority on the Bignoniaceae, writes: "We have one small plant of *Jacaranda chelonia*. This species, as you say, is definitely a dwarf. Contrary to other species of *Jacaranda*, we find that *J. chelonia* tends to flower freely each year. I would look forward to its being a very fine and reliable tubbed specimen for conservatory work. If you ever have more seed of it, we would be happy to attempt to raise more plants for our collection."

The color of the fallen corollas of the Stuart jacaranda, according to the Royal Horticultural Society's Color Chart, is Wistaria Blue 640/1 and this is faithfully reproduced here by the printer; however, with the sun shining through the flowers on the tree, they are a brighter, livelier hue. By contrast, the color of the flowers of the author's specimen of *J. mimosifolia* is Dauphin's Violet 039/1. In this species a wide variation of color is common, with many shades of blue and purple ranging to white. The white form is illustrated in color in Menninger's Flowering Trees of the World.

Jacaranda sp. (The Jacaranda without a Name)

Tecoma castanifolia (Golden Bells from Ecuador)

Golden Bells from Ecuador
(*Tecoma castanifolia*)

An exceptionally handsome little flowering tree that has been available in Florida for thirty years is rarely planted, because of a misunderstanding. This tree is *Tecoma castanifolia** from Ecuador.

Every Florida gardener from Jacksonville to Key West, on the other hand, is familiar with the ubiquitous yellow elder, *Stenolobium stans* Seemann. It is a weedy shrub, sometimes to 8 meters, seen more often in waste places than in gardens. Exceptionally handsome in flower, with quantities of musty-smelling golden bell flowers in ample clusters, it is objectionable in cultivation because (1) it seeds prolifically and these papery reminders, borne by the wind, come up all over the place; (2) its 15 cm.-long, pencil-like seed pods, in big bunches of 30 to 40, hang on the tree for many weeks and are not pretty; (3) the plant is deciduous sometimes for months, at a time of year when Floridians want their gardens to be in full dress.

Of course the "yellow elder" is not an elder, but belongs to the Bignoniaceae, with a lot of rich relatives like *Jacaranda, Tabebuia, Spathodea,* etc.

All this description of an unwanted cinderella is necessary to explain why the Ecuadorian tree has been neglected, or almost completely overlooked. The trouble is that *Tecoma castanifolia* at first glance does look like the yellow elder, and not enough persons have taken a second glance.

This *Tecoma,* however, is very different from the yellow elder in the following particulars.

(1) It does not sucker from the base and it is a tree, not a weedy shrub.

(2) It blooms every day in the year under ideal conditions—at least this is the record of a street specimen in Stuart, Florida, that the author grew from seed. It is the only tree on record in Florida as a year-round bloomer except the horseradish tree, *Moringa oleifera* (Linnaeus) Lamarck. Temperature lows of 28° F. (−2.2° C.) in December 1962 and again in February 1964 knocked off all the leaves and flowers but they were back in 60 days with no wood damage. No low-temperature survival records beyond this are available.

(3) The tree produces its golden bell flowers in smaller clusters in among the leaves. By contrast, the yellow elder is usually half-bare of leaves when it flowers and often the leaves cannot be seen for the masses of bloom, which lasts only a few days.

(4) The seed pods are extremely slender, the size of a darning needle, sometimes 13 cm. long, often produced singly or in 2's or 3's, so are never

---

Tecoma castanifolia (D. Don) Melchior. This new name in 1941 was based on D. Don's *Stenolobium castanifolium,* the oldest published name for the species. The tree was introduced into the United States in 1935 under the name *Tecoma Gaudichaudii* DC. and assigned the Plant Introduction number 107836. It came directly from Guayas Province, Ecuador, where it is truly native, though the introducer reported in error that it was native to Colombia.

conspicuous. Seeking seed requires really hunting for pods, for they are not easy to see.

(5) Here is a quick, easy way to tell the trees apart. On *Stenolobium* the leaves are trifoliate, in groups of three. On *Tecoma* the leaves are simple.

The specimen tree in Stuart which is pictured here is 10 years old, maintains its dwarf form and well-balanced crown without trimming, and demonstrates the usefulness of this stepchild as a full-sun street tree in warm regions. The originally established tree at the U.S. Plant Introduction Garden at Coconut Grove, Florida, is now 30 years old; it is 5 meters tall and has a spread of 6 meters. It flowers much less than the tree in Stuart, primarily in March.

Tecoma castanifolia (the specific name means it has leaves like a chestnut) is cultivated under greenhouse conditions at Longwood Gardens, Kennett Square, Pennsylvania, where Dr. R. J. Seibert, Director, reports: "We have found this species far superior to the yellow elder. *T. castanifolia* blooms regularly and has a very fine inflorescence of good, clear, yellow flowers."

Noel Y. Sandwith, of the Royal Botanic Gardens, Kew, another distinguished authority on the Bignoniaceae, says: "I regard *T. castanifolia* as a good species. It is a very local species of the Pacific Coast of Ecuador."

Melchior, in adopting the name *Tecoma castanifolia,*[*] cited only the synonomy, with no description. The original description[**] was published by D. Don: "Calyx small, bell-shaped, 5-toothed, equal. Base of corolla narrowly tubular; limb 5-lobed, equal, 2-lipped. Stamens 4, fertile, a fifth rudimentary. Anther lobes linear, thin, compressed, bilocular. Seeds smooth, transverse, with membranous margins. Wide-branched Peruvian tree, erect, leaves simple, opposite, resembling those of chestnut, elliptic, coriaceous, acute, veins at right angle to midrib, petiolate, with serrate margins, lower surface copiously clothed with a stellate tomentum, 2-3 inches wide, glabrous above. Flowers terminal, numerous, spicatepaniculate, reddish purple [sic!], similar in size to Jacaranda. Style shorter than the stamens. Stigma bilamellate. Capsule 5-parted."

---

[*]Berichte der Deutchen Botanischen Gesellschaft 59: 26. 1941.
[**]Edinburgh Philosophical Journal 9: 264. 1823.

Millettia—Jewels on a String*

Millettia trees are almost unknown in cultivation in the United States, despite the fact that there are a hundred and twenty different species scattered through Burma and Assam, Malaya, Australia, and Tropical Africa, and many of them are exceedingly lovely in bloom. They were named after a French botanist, J. A. Millet, and are mostly tall evergreen forest trees that bear in spring delicate, drooping strings of the most daintily tinted flowers, usually mauve, steel blue, lazuli blue, or rose, much resembling Wisteria.

All the species described here and a few others unidentified are now in actual cultivation in the United States, but only the first two have bloomed. In California *Millettia caffra* from Natal, South Africa, is sparingly grown. It is a very ornamental small tree with striking purple flowers in summer followed by large velvet-brown seed pods.

Millettia ovalifolia. Native of the Promc district of Burma, has been flowering nicely in Florida the past several years, from the middle of March when the tree is bare, through the middle of April with the new leaves unfolding along with the blossoms. Benthall in *Trees of Calcutta* starts out by calling this "a very beautiful little tree" and then he goes on to say that it is "one of the most beautiful of trees when covered with its delicate sprays of flowers before the leaves appear." In Florida, it certainly lives up to this enthusiastic estimate of its worth. Much of the effectiveness of the bloom lies in the two-color effect, for the sepals are Garnet Lake 828 and the petals are Magenta Rose O27/1. (RHC). It has a rounded crown, neat growth habit, half-drooping branches, and elegant foliage consisting of seven thin, smooth, pointed, bright green leaflets arranged in three opposite pairs on either side of a slender midrib with a terminal leaflet at the tip.

The following species are growing in Stuart, Florida, but are not yet old enough to bloom:

M. dura. Fast-growing shrub or tree to 35 feet, with hanging clusters of lilac, Wisteria-like flowers, three or four strings together, 4 to 8 inches long. Eggeling: *Indigenous Trees of Uganda* says this "handsome" species is frequently planted in gardens. Jex-Blake: *Gardening in East Africa* says the tree is quick growing, flowers in three years, resists drought and white ants, flowers abundantly but is liable to damage by wind.

M. stuhlmanni. From Mozambique, Portuguese East Africa, is a tree to 15 feet high, irregular in shape, not too dense, with four pairs of oblong 5-inch leaflets, with "very attractive" lavender flowers, according to a letter from the Department of Agriculture at Inhambane. It adds: "Good for street planting."

Millettia sp. From Durban, South Africa, botanic garden, grown from seed received in 1944 with this description: "This un-named small Millettia tree has rather an upright habit and bears spikes of pink flowers, somewhat like Wisteria."

M. pendula. An erect tree from Burma, with dull green leaves about 6 inches long, the leaflets 2 to 3 inches long. The white flowers are in short dense clusters in the leaf axils.

97. MILLETTIA OVALIFOLIA

98. MILLETTIA RETICULATA

Cassia—the Golden Shower and Its Handsome Relatives

Among the most widely grown ornamentals in Florida are the cassias or "shower" trees, many of which are exceptionally beautiful when in bloom. The genus, belonging to the pea family or Leguminosae, contains four hundred species, including many shrubs; it is confined almost entirely to tropical areas. The reader should not confuse this name with cassia buds, cassia oil, Chinese cassia, *Cassia lignea*, or any of the other names given to spices derived from trees of the laurel family or Lauraceae. There is no relationship between them, just a confusion of names. Careless pronunciation also causes many persons to confuse cassia with acacia, an entirely different genus of almost seven hundred trees and shrubs of the related order Mimosaceae.

Most of the showy-flowered cassias, which are cultivated in gardens all over the world, bear yellow five-petalled flowers, sometimes in drooping sprays but often in clusters or spikes above the foliage. A dozen or more pink-flowered species are distinguished for their delicate beauty, and red and white-flowered trees are not uncommon. Notably in Hawaii and India, cross-breeding has produced hybrids, both natural and artificial, that bear multi-colored flowers and have given rise to the popular name "rainbow shower." Profusion of bloom has accounted for the descriptive names "golden shower" and "bronze shower" and so on. However, to avoid confusion, the accepted common name for all cassia trees is senna, as this drug is derived from different species.

Best known of the cassias, because it is grown for its lovely flowers in every warm country, is the Indian tree, golden shower senna (*C. fistula*), which is variously known as pudding pipe tree, purging cassia, and Indian laburnum. It is handsome in form, the crown spreading and open, though when mature rather heavy for a cassia. It grows slowly and rarely exceeds thirty feet in height, blooming when much smaller.

The golden shower senna is classed as deciduous, although even in winter it is almost never entirely leafless, and the bare period is short. In tropical lands, as in Singapore where there is no cold season, a complete leaf-change takes place at intervals of nine or ten months. The compound leaves, twelve to eighteen inches long, comprise four to eight pairs of four-inch leaflets, rather larger than those of most cassias. The color of the leaves varies markedly with the make-up of the soil, ranging from a glossy dark green to a light, soft yellow-green. In some types the new foliage is a rich copper or even a chocolate color, slightly fuzzy.

The lovely fragrant flowers, which make this "the finest of all cassias," are produced in the greatest profusion in hanging sprays one foot or more long. The translucent color ranges from pale primrose to golden-yellow. The individual flowers are somewhat irregular—according to Ida Colthurst in Familiar Flowering Trees in India, "one of the petals being almost like the standard in the pea flower and, strangely enough, imitating it in screening the other parts by turning its back to the wind." The stamens drop early, the petals remaining fresh for a considerable time; the tree, when in flower in

100. CASSIA MULTIJUGA

99. CASSIA EXCELSA

102. CASSIA FISTULA

101. CASSIA FISTULA (Golden Shower tree)

104. CASSIA PETERSIANA

103. CASSIA NODOSA (Pink Shower)

May and June, is very beautiful. We are told by Alpinus, when he was in Egypt in the latter part of the sixteenth century, that the natives took great delight in walking early in the morning at certain seasons near plantations of this cassia, regaling themselves with the fragrance of its flowers.

The cylindrical seed pods, two to three feet long and less than one inch in diameter, hang green on the tree, turning black as they ripen after ten months. They are divided transversely into numerous compartments, each containing one seed embedded in a brown sticky pulp of characteristic licorice-like odor, and of medicinal value for its laxative properties.

The pods are so durable that the seeds never germinate naturally, unless or until the pods are broken by animals or other external means. Even then, though viable for two years or more, the seeds germinate tardily. In garden propagation, soaking the seeds five minutes in boiling water to break the tough shell is found advisable. Often they are dropped into a glass of boiling water and allowed to soak overnight or longer.

The golden shower senna is not frost hardy. In its native habitat the temperature range is 25°–65° minimum to 100°–120° maximum. The rainfall range in the same areas is twenty to one hundred twenty inches, which makes this tree well suited for planting in dry regions; it is notably drought resistant. Nor is the tree gregarious even in India—there are scattered specimens here and there in the forest, occasionally in light shade which this cassia tolerates.

Many other yellow-flowered cassias are cultivated for ornament in various parts of the world—South and Central America, Asia, tropical Africa—but none so extensively as the golden shower senna. Noteworthy among these is: *Cassia alata,* called candlestick senna because the inflorescences are erect, candelabra-like clusters of black buds. The deep yellow-orange flowers open from the base upwards over a period of several weeks in November and December. This shrubby cassia, which is native to tropical America, attains a height of only eight feet. A quick-growing tree, to sixty feet, is *C. spectabilis.* It is very conspicuous in late fall, when it bears profusely two-foot clusters of bright yellow flowers resembling calceolarias. *C. siamia,* from Asia, is a better shade tree than most of the cassias. It grows fast, thrives on dry laterite soil, crowds out weeds, and is useful in recovering waste areas. The flowers are borne in pyramidal clusters, rarely showy, in October–November and continue over a long period. The most promising winter-flowering species is *C. goratensis* from West Africa.

Many regard the pink-flowered cassias as more beautiful than the commoner yellow-flowered trees. Certainly they are more difficult to grow; at least this would seem to be true in Florida.

Confusion surrounds the identity of the three best-known species, partly because of differences of opinion among botanists, partly because of carelessness with names, and partly because natural hybrids have developed which do not conform to textbook descriptions.

The jointwood senna (*C. nodosa*), often referred to as "pink-and-white shower" because of the presence of a few white petals, is a medium-sized, deciduous, Indian tree requiring full sun. The two and a quarter inch, deep rose, sweetly-scented flowers, which appear in dense heads on the branches behind the leaves, have yellow stamens and a brown stigma. The stipules are tiny.

105. CASSIA GORATENSIS

106. CASSIA SPECTABILIS

Their color fades with age.

The appleblossom senna (*C. javanica*) is a small Malayan tree which, after a bare season, puts out fresh foliage in April or May, accompanied by masses of rosy pink flowers closely resembling large apple blossoms. In contrast with the previous entry, the flowers of *C. javanica* are larger, are a lighter pink, have no odor, have a green stigma, and come at the ends of leafy twigs. The stipules are large. Moreover, this tree usually has spines here and there on its trunk, and it has very long, drooping branches. It grows rapidly when once established, tolerates no shade, and benefits by sharp pruning. The brown cylindrical seed pods, one to two feet long, are not plentifully produced. Both *C. nodosa* and *C. javanica* have five to twelve pairs of elliptic leaflets, which are broadest at the middle. Corner, in WAYSIDE TREES OF MALAYA, says *C. javanica* and *C. nodosa* are extremes of the same species. In FLORA HAWAIIENSIS, Otto Degener writes: "These two scientific names do not apply to two distinct species: *C. nodosa* is a synonym of *C. javanica* or, more likely, is the incorrect name of a plant that should be called *Cassia javanica* var. *nodosa*. This last is said to bear leaflets having usually a rounded or retuse apex, while typical *C. javanica* seems to have mostly acute to acuminate leaflets." Marie C. Neal says, IN GARDENS OF HAWAII, *C. javanica* and *C. nodosa* are synonyms for the same species.

There probably are no mature trees of the Burmese senna (*Cassia renigera*) in Florida, although many are now being grown from seeds imported from India. Some persons may dispute this, without being aware that the magnificent tree on the Col. Robert H. Montgomery place in Coconut Grove, for many years believed to be *C. renigera*, was definitely identified several years ago by no less an authority than E. J. H. Corner, author of WAYSIDE TREES OF MALAYA (often called the finest tropical tree book in print). Mr. Corner, who was on the staff of the Singapore Botanical Garden for ten years, saw Col. Montgomery's tree in full bloom and identified it definitely as *C. javanica*. Hundreds of seedlings of this tree have been scattered all over Florida under the name of *C. renigera;* it was an honest mistake which misled novices and experts alike.

The Burmese senna is very similar to *C. nodosa* except that the flowers are larger, a richer pink and more showy, and the calyx is densely hairy. The softly hairy leaflets number thirteen to twenty pairs, are oblong and parallel sided. The stipules are large, leafy, kidney shaped (the "ren" of the specific name is latin for kidney) and one half to one inch long. Kathleen Gough in her GARDEN BOOK FOR MALAYA calls it "the most beautiful of all cassias." It grows and flowers well in moist areas although, in its natural habitat, it is accustomed to a dry climate and is capable of growing in comparatively poor soil. The flowers are usually pink, but yellow blossoms are not unknown.

The pink shower senna (*C. grandis*), often referred to as horse cassia, is a large spreading Central American tree, sometimes to one hundred feet, with long, coarse leaves having ten to twenty pairs of rather large leaflets that are dark green above, light green below. During March and April, the pink shower senna produces seven-inch clusters of flowers (one inch in diameter) in great abundance, rose-pink with yellow throat on first opening, changing to salmon with age. The flowers are rarely white. The bark of the tree is chocolate brown

108. CASSIA MARGINATA

107. CASSIA RENIGERA

and scaly. Standley says: "When in flower, this is one of the handsome trees of Central America, especially along the Pacific lowlands, reminding one of apple trees, by both the form of the tree and the coloring of the blossoms." The seed pods are blackish brown, eighteen inches long, one and a half inches in diameter, rounded with two longitudinal ridges on one side and one on the other. The one-half inch seeds are imbedded in sweet, offensive-smelling pulp.

The bronze shower senna (*C. moschata*) is a tall, spreading, deciduous South American tree to seventy-five feet, with fifteen-inch compound leaves which are brown when quite young, changing through delicate shades to dark green. After a rest period of two months without leaves, the tree in March bears eight to ten-inch, hanging clusters of "very pretty" one-inch flowers, produced just before or simultaneously with new foliage. The flower calyx is deep, reddish brown and the unequal petals are a combination of yellow and orange-red.

The ceylon senna (*C. marginata*) has spreading, drooping boughs which are decorated in spring with quantities of clustering, fragrant blooms ranging in tone from white through pink to a deep rose and marked with greenish veins. It is a slow-growing tree of graceful habit, blooming after the third year if planted in the sun. Its specific name arises from the colored and thickened margins of the leaves. The slender cylindrical seed pod is ten inches long.

Other pink-flowered cassia trees are to be found in the tropics, many of them worthy of cultivation. In Brazil, *C. leptophylla* is widely planted in parks and gardens and along avenues because of its highly ornamental value. This thirty-foot tree bears great quantities of pink flowers on long flexuous branches. Peru offers *C. scarlatina* with "petals scarlet or brick-red or white and red," as well as *C. rubiflora* with "petals blood-red and yellow" and *C. swartzioides* with flowers "white marked with rose below." In Siam there is a pink-flowered species, *C. bakeriana*. In Australia, the flowers of *C. brewteri* are "very conspicuous deep red and yellow."

Multicolored blossoms resulting from crosses of the yellow and pink species have fascinated growers for many years, particularly in India and Hawaii, and some small efforts in this field have been made in Florida and Cuba.

S. Percy Lancaster, secretary of the Royal Agri-Horticultural Society of India, at Calcutta, says: "Several hybrids are in existence but none can be depended on to reproduce themselves true from seed. These three hybrids deserve mention: *Alipurense,* with cream-colored flowers like *C. fistula* but borne in greater profusion: *Atkinsiana,* intermediate between *C. fistula* and *C. nodosa,* spikes pendant though short, flowers cream-yellow with red sepals; *Lancasteri,* a hybrid between *C. nodosa* and *C. marginata* (*C. roxburghi*), intermediate in color but flowering right through the rains."

In Hawaii the cassia hybrids are called rainbow shower. Kuck & Tongg write of them in THE TROPICAL GARDEN, "These trees vary widely among themselves. The flowers are usually of a prevailing apricot tone, although individual flowers on the same branch may differ considerably. Some of the seedling colors are beautiful and others are rather muddy. Layering and inarching from specimens which are desired are two ways to be sure of getting a tree of satisfactory color. The form of the tree is also variable, being generally larger and

109. CASSIA CARNAVAL

110. CASSIA JAVANICA (Pink-and-white Shower)

more spreading than *C. fistula*."

Degener says: ". . . probably the most beautiful of these (hybrids) is a specimen growing in Kamanele Park near the University of Hawaii. This resembles most closely *C. fistula*. Though producing an abundance of pods, the seeds of this hybrid are deformed."

J. A. Johnston, one of the pioneer hybridizers of hibiscus in Hawaii, shortly before his death in 1946, wrote a letter to the "Honolulu Advertiser" about the propagation of cassia trees, in which he was critical of inarching. His letter said in part:

"This ancient Chinese method of propagation requires too much time and labor, and I was surprised that it was recommended to the ladies of the park board. It is not difficult to graft these trees and I know several people who have done it. Some years ago I grafted some scions, taken from seedling trees on Farrington Street, on to *Cassia grandis* (pink and white shower) and the next year while still in large tins, these young grafted trees threw blooms.

"*Cassia grandis* and *C. nodosa* are both strong growers and I am betting two to one that grafted plants of rainbows or any of the others will be much more satisfactory and become stronger trees.

"To any who do not know what the process of airlayering is—we'll say that the propagator goes up into a tree, selects a branch he wants, cuts away a ring of bark, builds up a pile of mud and moss (the size of a plum pudding), builds it around the branch where the ring of bark was cut away, wraps a piece of bagging around it, then prays that the branch will like the pudding well enough to throw out roots."

Cassia trees have several things in common:

(1) Most of them grow well on relatively poor soil, often under very dry conditions.

(2) They benefit from severe pruning and survive windstorms with small damage, if thinned well after flowering.

(3) The fresh tissues, especially the bark, in most species has a foetid smell like crushed bean pods.

(4) In some localities senna trees will not fruit. Harrison Smith reported from Tahiti that with twelve species of *Cassia*, only two ever spontaneously produced seed and only one other responded to efforts at pollination.

The common "shower trees"—they get that name from the falling petals—are less resistant to cold as one of their brothers—an Argentine tree which grows to 18 feet known as *Cassia carnaval*. When it flowers all spring and summer it certainly puts on a carnival of golden bloom, good enough to justify its name.

The tree bears lots of seed, it grows fast, and it will repay your trouble many times over.

112. BOMBAX ELLIPTICUM (Shaving Brush)

111. CEIBA PENTANDRA (Kapok)

Gigantic Bombax Splashes Landscape With
Mass of Crimson Flowers

Probably the best known of Indian flowering trees is the Red Silk Cotton (*Bombax malabaricum*), which is found throughout India and Burma, except in the driest spots.

This tree makes a magnificent splash of color through the early Spring. Its brilliant crimson, close-set, four-inch flowers burst from their dark buds and cover the branches of the trees when they are bare of leaves—providing a striking blaze on the landscape. The spectacle is enhanced by the symmetry of the whorled branches, tier above tier, like a gigantic upside-down candelabra. The individual cup blossoms are filled with scarlet stamens almost as long as the petals, each tipped with a purple anther.

The Bombax is not an uncommon tree in South Florida, where it was introduced more than 50 years ago, but it grows to such gigantic proportions that it is suited only to parks or wide parkways. There is a specimen on Lake Trail in Palm Beach that is nearly eight feet in diameter at the base and 100 feet high. There are similar huge trees in Miami and near Clearwater. In dry spots, the growth is stunted, but with plenty of moisture available the tree often exceeds 100 feet. Marshall recorded a tree at the foot of the Coorg ghats in India, where rainfall is 190 inches a year, that was 195 feet high and 102 feet in girth three feet above the ground. This tree had seven buttresses so large that an elephant could easily hide between any two of them.

Bombax flowers secrete a nectar that is very attractive to birds, as well as various insects, and the fallen flowers that form a scarlet carpet on the ground are greedily eaten by squirrels, deer and other animals. In Burma the fleshy calyces are gathered as they fall and much relished by the natives as a curry vegetable.

The fruit of the Bombax is a six-inch pod that splits open on the tree and disgorges quantities of silky cotton in which the small seeds are imbedded. The bursting pods cover the neighborhood with drifting floss and it is carried far by the winds. This cotton is occasionally gathered in India and used for pillow stuffing, in much the same way that all countries use kapok—the floss from a related tree, *Ceiba pentandra*, that has unattractive, dirty-white flowers and is not an ornamental. The so-called "kapok tree" at the Sumner B. Covey citrus grove on Road 593 near Safety Harbor, Florida, is a Bombax, and not the true kapok at all—the picture postcards to the contrary notwithstanding. It stands 145 feet high; the base measures 41 feet in circumference. The tree was planted in 1888.

The usual color of Bombax flowers is crimson, but Lancaster records that in India the shades tone down on occasional trees to a deep orange-yellow which is quite uncommon.

Here's the best way to tell Bombax from Ceiba: (1) Bombax has a deep-red under bark; (2) the stalks of the leaflets on Bombax are one inch long, but are very short on Ceiba.

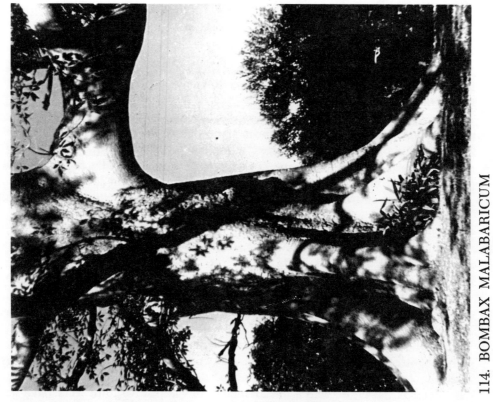

114. BOMBAX MALABARICUM

113. BOMBAX MALABARICUM

The five-to-seven digitate leaflets are much alike on these two trees, and there are some unidentified trees of this same family being cultivated in South Florida with yellowish tubular flowers. Much the same foliage prevails on *Chorisia* trees, and the leaves of *Sterculia foetida* are similar (though the branches are not in whorls). So do not jump quickly to the identification of trees in this family; there are at least 60 different kinds of Bombax trees, some already introduced in South Florida, some with pure white flowers and some with flowers of other colors.

The wood provided by the quick-growing Bombax tree unfortunately has little commercial value. It is too soft to have much character, and it has to be sawed into boards as soon as it's cut or it splits and becomes worthless. Its chief use in India is in making matches. In some places, Bombax logs are hollowed out and used as canoes.

The Bombax is a light demander, so when the seed sprouts in the forest, it jumps quickly to the top of the green canopy. This produces a straight trunk, which under forest conditions is often 80 feet or more to the first branches. The bark is smooth and gray, and when the tree is young it is often covered with conical prickles. These disappear with age and are replaced gradually by smooth, heavy buttresses. Seedlings are fire resistant; often when burned back by grass fires they will sprout again from the root. Mature trees have a thick bark and once established are seldom damaged by fire.

Bombax trees are easily grown from seed. Or with a spade you can cut a root under one of the big trees and when a sprout is sent up, this can be dug and re-established elsewhere without difficulty.

Incidentally, *Bombax malabaricum* DC is described in some Indian books under the name *Salmalia malabarica* Schott. et Enal.

B. *reflexum* (Uganda). Very striking, splendid (red) flowers.

B. *munguba* (Peru). Flowers white, large and conspicuous.

B. *rhodophagnalon* (Kenya). Flowers showy, large; 4-inch petals greenish-white, stamens red.

B. *stenopetalum* (Brazil). Large white flowers, in magnificent contrast to the dark-green foliage.

B. *insigne* (British Guiana). Striking trees, great blossoms nearly a foot in diameter.

B. *ellipticum* (Mexico). Petals purplish, stamens pink or white. Handsome flowers esteemed by the Mexicans as one of their most beautiful flowers.

B. *flavescens* (Brazil). Its yellow flowers and its foliage are beautiful.

B. *barrigon* (Panama). White flowers are conspicuous.

116. BALSA LOG

115. OCHROMA LAGOPUS (Balsa)

Balsa (*Ochroma lagopus*)—Not the Lightest Wood

Perhaps no tree is known to so many people, young and old, as the balsa from South America. Its chief claim to fame is lightness of the wood (specific gravity .12), about one-ninth the weight of water and half as heavy as cork, but it is commercially important too because of its great strength. Pound for pound it is stronger than oak.

Most of the balsa wood in commerce is produced in Ecuador where the trees are in groves. Foresters build railroads into the woody areas to bring out the logs, cutting one day a stand of balsa, another day moving on into a stand of hardwoods, for the balsa groves are scattered. Some balsa logs are rafted down the rivers.

When balsa trees are cut, the logs are heavy. They consist of very coarse cells which are full of sap. It is important that the logs be picked up immediately and stood on end to allow the sap to drain out of them. If the balsa log is allowed to lie on the forest floor, decay will begin within 48 hours. After the sap has drained away, a 20-foot log will weigh only about a hundred pounds. Loggers lift them easily to their shoulders. In this condition they are still difficult to saw—they behave like angel food cake under a dull knife. The end of a balsa log, as it goes into the sawmill, has no annual rings, like other trees, because it grows continuously and does not stop once a year to rest.

The word balsa is a Spanish name for raft, for the dried logs are often used to build rafts on South American rivers. The Indians load their harvested fruits on a balsa raft, float it downstream to the nearest port where they sell everything, including the raft. The botanical name for the tree which supplies balsa wood is *Ochroma lagopus*, (Syn.: *O. pyramidale*). A tree 15 years old has passed maturity; the foresters try to cut them when they are about 10 years old. The leaves on the tree are roundish and very flat, often 15 inches or more in diameter. The tree's flowers are great white trumpets, rather handsome, and the seed pods are 8-inch fuzzy "beans" that are filled with brown fibres that are used in Ecuador for pillow stuffing but the fibres are too short for commercial use. The seeds are buried in this floss.

Balsa trees are occasionally grown in South Florida but they are usually too tall and skinny to be used in landscaping and they are essentially a "weed tree"—just grown to be cut.

The lightest of all woods, contrary to popular belief, is not balsa. Doubtless responsible for this misconception is the fact that balsa is the commonest lightweight wood with which most persons have had experience.

But balsa is far from being the lightest. Here are five trees which have lighter wood. How much lighter can be seen from the specific gravity figures:

Aeschynomene hispida Willd., sp. gr. .044. This wood weighs only one-third as much as balsa. It is a Cuban tree, allied in the bean family to *Sesbania* and *Daubentonia*. The pith helmets used in India are made from a species of this same genus.

117. OCHROMA LAGOPUS (Balsa)

118. OCHROMA LAGOPUS

Alstonia spathulata Bl., sp. gr. .058. This weighs half as much as balsa. Samples were discovered as driftwood on a Pacific island by the Japanese and for a time considerable mystery surrounded them because the wood of this *Alstonia* tree is not ordinarily so light. Researchers discovered that the light-weight wood is found underground in the tree's roots. Where the trunk joins the roots there is a marked swelling so that the diameter of a six-inch trunk may increase to twenty-four inches near the ground. The density of the wood in this swelling is about midway between the rather hard wood of the trunk and that of the almost pithy root. Root wood is so soft it can easily be indented with the finger nail.

Herminiera elaphroxylon Guill. et Perr., sp. gr. .065. This tree is from the banks of the Nile in tropical Africa where the wood is used for canoes. The timber is only half as heavy as balsa.

Cavanillesia platanifolia H. B. K., sp. gr. .103. This is a handsome tree of the Panama Canal Zone, growing often to a hundred feet. Standley called it "one of the most remarkable trees of this region" and added: "The tree . . . is very conspicuous, especially when in flower, in late March and early April." The red-petaled flowers are small. The wood is white or yellowish, soft, coarse, and pith like. No commercial use is made of it, but the trunks are often used by the natives for canoes, or to float rafts of hardwood which would otherwise sink to the bottom. The timber is sixteen percent lighter than balsa.

Annona palustris L., sp. gr. .116. This "root wood" from Cuba is allied to the custard apple and soursop trees of Florida, all of them rather small of stature. The wood is only a fraction lighter than balsa.

119. WERCKLEA INSIGNIS

120. THESPESIA POPULNEA (Portia tree)

WERCKLEA—A Costa Rican Mallow

"Beautiful and ornamental. . . . One of the most interesting and showy trees of Costa Rica," is Dr. Paul Standley's description of a mallow named *Wercklea insignis* which has been established in Florida and southern California. As the 2-inch bristly capsules contain plenty of seeds that germinate readily, the plant doubtless will be widely grown in warm regions because of its "tropical" appearance.

The bright green kidney-shaped, palmately-veined leaves are from 8 to 16 inches across, spreading away from the branches on thick green to reddish stalks. Because the tree is evergreen and its foliage so heavy, it makes a conspicuous garden plant all year. It compels even more attention from February to April (in Florida) when it produces its huge, solitary, hibiscus-like flowers, 5 inches across, on stalks to 6 inches long. Standley's "Flora of Costa Rica" calls the color "rose-lilac with a yellow base," but by the Royal Horticultural Society chart, the blooms produced in Florida have a throat that is Persian Rose 628, while the petal lips are Magnolia Purple o3o/3.

Wercklea insignis makes a tree of 20 to 35 feet, and its pale thin-barked trunk may be 12 inches in diameter. No records are available on its frost hardiness. Although this is the only species so far established in the United States, Standley reports another species in Costa Rica. *W. lutea*, a similar but smaller tree (10 to 20 feet), with the corolla yellow, and he adds: "Even showier than *W. insignis* because of the bright color of the flowers, which suggest pumpkin blossoms. In form the flowers much resemble those of the hollyhock."

122. PLUMERIA SP. (Yellow)

121. PLUMERIA SP. (White) (Frangipani)

Plumeria (Frangipani)—a Tree of Tropical America

The only tree representative of the periwinkle family, Apocynaceae, to find a common place in Florida gardens, is the frangipani. The gouty, soft-barked trunk and the gray, non-tapering branches that are more conspicuous than the foliage, make it the ugly duckling of the tropical garden, saved from oblivion only by the exquisite and often heavy fragrance of its waxy flowers which rival both the jasmines and the gardenias. Yet of all the ornamental tropical plants with large fragrant flowers, the frangipani is the easiest to grow. A branch stuck in the ground (in February) usually needs no further attention. As a result, this native of tropical America is extensively cultivated in every warm country around the globe.

The odd name frangipani is applied with abandon to any of the perhaps forty-five species of *Plumeria* (often incorrectly spelled *Plumiera* or *Plumieria*) which was named after a seventeenth century botanist, Charles Plumier. Some experts believe there are not more than ten species and everybody agrees that all of them are confused and inadequately understood.

The two kinds most commonly encountered in Florida are the Mexican frangipani (*P. acuminata*) with yellow-centered white flowers, and the nosegay frangipani (*P. rubra*) which usually has pink or red blossoms. A red leaf stalk sometimes serves as an identification mark. But as Corner says, *P. rubra* "is a convenient name for the pink and red-flowered varieties of which there are many, differing in the size and shape of the leaves and the flower and the intensity of its color. It has yet to be discovered whether these varieties represent a species or a group of hybrids between other species." Neal points to the crossing of *P. rubra* "resulting in plants bearing flowers with various combinations of white, rose and yellow." Britton reports that *P. rubra* may be purple, while Bailey records the color as "more or less rosy" or a golden color with pink tips on the petals. To the layman the names simmer down to a grand confusion!

Everybody agrees to the common name frangipani (sometimes spelled frangipanni) but whether its origin was from the French word frangipanier, meaning sour milk, or whether the tree was "discovered by Frangipani, the botanist, when he landed in Antigua with the Columbus expedition," or whether it was to honor an Italian nobleman named Frangipani who compounded a perfume which the scent of these tropical flowers resembled, nobody knows or cares.

Many other common names are prevalent in tropical countries, for although native of tropical America, the trees are grown in many other lands where similar conditions prevail. They have been cultivated in Asia at least 200 years, probably not for ornament, however, as much as for the medicinal properties attributed by many to the sticky milk that pours from a wound on the tree. In Malaya they are planted in cemeteries more frequently than in gardens and hence are commonly called "graveyard flowers." In India the Mohammedan graveyards are filled with frangipani trees and in Ceylon it is

124. PLUMERIA SP. (Multi-color)

123. PLUMERIA SP. (Pink)

called "The Life Tree." It is a favorite in Buddhist worship, being regarded as an emblem of immortality, because of its wonderful power of leafing and even blooming when out of the soil, if kept in the shade. In Hawaii the trees are called "Melia" (though not related to the botanical genus of that name). In Porto Rico, the common name is "Paucipan;" in India "Pogoda Tree" or Temple Tree."

Frangipani trees are prized exclusively for their flowers which come in crowded clusters at the tips of the branches, last a long time on the tree, continue to resist wilt after picking much longer than most tropical blossoms, and hence lend themselves for use in making leis in Hawaii, garlands for temple offerings in India, or bouquets in Florida. The exquisite fragrance persists even after the blossoms fall from the trees. The odor of the flowers is as strong in one color as another, is most noticeable at evening, may be almost entirely absent in midday. "The beautiful sweet-scented flowers were a favorite among the ancient Mexican people who often plant them in their gardens and use the flowers for decorations, especially in churches. The Indians often wear them in their hair."

Frangipani trees are usually small, rarely exceeding twenty-five feet and often blooming when only two feet high, if the rooted cutting was a branch tip. Cuttings should be allowed to dry out for a week before being planted and are more satisfactory than propagation from seed. Most frangipani trees set seed in six-inch twin pods that are first green, then black, but much of it is infertile. In Florida, the trees are leafless when flowering begins in March. The flowering may continue for months; the new leaves gradually return as the blossoms drop' away. In Singapore some species are evergreen or only partly deciduous. In Hawaii, the blooming continues nearly all the year.

They thrive in dry and rocky situations, resist salty seabreezes well and do not shatter in hurricane winds. If toppled over, they go right on growing and blooming when pushed back up again. Large trees to twenty feet, with practically no roots, can be moved to new locations without wilting or decline. The spreading habit of the crown can be checked by trimming away the out-reaching branches, leaving only those which go upwards.

Ida Colthurst, in her interesting book, *Familiar Flowering Trees in India* writes of the frangipani: "For all its fragrance, the frangipani is not exactly what one would consider an artistic tree, and time was when I vigorously excluded it from my garden, but one day I came upon Waterfield's eulogy of it in his 'Ballads,' and now, for the very beauty of his ideas and the music of the poem, it is one of my favorites."

Despite the confusion of botanical names and the variation in trees described by different authorities, the following outline may serve as a general guide to the species usually encountered:

P. acuminata (syn. *P. acutifolia*) has white flowers with yellow centers. Gough says the blossoms are "slightly pink on the outer side." Corner says there is a pinkish streak on the inside of each petal. The leaves are narrower than *P. rubra*.

P. rubra has red or pink flowers as previously related. Both it and the

157

preceding have long pointed leaves.

P. obtusa and *P. emarginata* from Cuba have blunt ends on the leaves and white flowers. These two species are closely allied and may prove identical. *P. obtusa* is more robust than *P. acuminata* and has darker green leaves.

P. sericifolia has less showy white flower clusters, and the under sides of the leaves are densely hairy.

P. alba is a white-flowered "low tree," not as showy as some other species, but appears to be evergreen, at least in Hawaii. It has a distinctive leaf, narrow in relation to its length (often 1½ x 8 inches), the margins curled downward and the leaf crinkled as if being attacked by aphids, the tip sharp, and the characteristic marginal vein around the edge of the leaf absent or almost so. There are a few plants in Florida.

P. lutea has flowers similar to those of *P. acuminata* but larger, nearly four inches across and "very sweet smelling." There are a few specimens in cultivation in California.

P. tricolor has flowers that are pink and yellow within, and red and white without. This species is cultivated in Mexico and Singapore. It might easily be confused with some of the *P. rubra* hybrids.

There are a good many shrubs and vines of the periwinkle family in North American gardens. Among these are allamanda, crape jasmine (*Ervatamia*), natal plum (*Carissa*), oleander (*Nerium*) and, of course, periwinkle (*Vinca*). There are other trees, too, besides frangipani, such as the "yellow Oleander" (*Thevetia*), *Ochrosia* and the scholar tree (*Alstonia*) but except for *Thevetia*, they are comparatively rare.

126. BIXA ORELLANA (Lipstick tree)

125. OCHNA

OCHNA—What's That?

Florida garden lovers are just beginning to get acquainted with a group of shrubs and small trees from Asia and tropical Africa that comprise the genus *Ochna*. Their chief value on our landscape lies in the fact that with us they are winter bloomers, covering themselves first with showy, bright yellow flowers, and later with vivid red-and-black seed displays that are equally conspicuous.

It is too early to form an opinion of which kind of *Ochna* is going to be most satisfactory in Florida gardens. An African species that is usually called "Birdseye bush" (*Ochna multiflora*) is cultivated in southern California almost exclusively and there it makes a handsome, bushy shrub to 5 feet. It seems to do exceeding well in Florida also, is hardy through the central part of the State and produces plenty of flowers and seedpods. But at least four other kinds of *Ochna* are under cultivation in South Florida, and some of them show great promise. Scattered over Asia and Africa there are some 90 species, most of them with bright yellow flowers, but Ridley in "The Flora of the Malaya Peninsula," reports that the flowers in the family are "showy—green, white, red or yellow."

Perhaps the African species that puts on the biggest show with its huge seed displays is *O.schweinfurthiana*, but unfortunately the seeds of this so far received in Florida have failed to germinate. In all the *Ochna*, the seeds are contained in the black berry, and this is surrounded by brilliant red, fleshy calyces that look like petals. In *O.schweinfurthiana* the berry and the calyces are extra large.

A similar brilliant display is put on by *O.mossambicensis* which is becoming more common in Florida as the result of its introduction by Fairchild Tropical Garden and other agencies. The yellow flowers are 1½ inches across, the petals soon dropping, and then the persistent scarlet sepals take over 'til the seeds are ripe. This plant produces such abundant quantities of flowers along the branches, as to make it a striking object. Ordinarily a shrub, it often becomes a small tree to 10 feet.

Also sometimes seen in Florida is a closely related species, *Ochna kirkii* which some believe may be only a variety of *O.mosambicensis*. At any rate it has much larger leaves, up to 5 inches, whereas the others are 2 to 3 inches.

Another species established in Florida is *O.thomasiana*, from Zanzibar. It has simple, stiff, shining, oval 2 inch leaves with many tiny, inconspicuous spines on the margins. The 1½ inch yellow flowers are short-lived, the petals dropping by afternoon of the day they open. Williams in his book on Zanzibar and Pemba, writes: "After flowering, the 5-lobed calyx becomes bright red, about 1 inch diameter, and surrounds a red, cushion-like receptacle upon which are borne several black fruit about the size of peas; a most attractive arrangement."

Florida gardeners will do well to watch for *Ochna* and try growing it as a winter season ornament.

Erythrina—Let's End the Confusion About the Coral Tree

If you have a "coral tree" in your yard, and a visitor insists on calling it an "Immortelle," and you are little bothered anyway about the name of this pretty, red-flowered creature, you will be joining the elect. For even the experts are confused and confounded over the 35 species of *Erythrina*, nearly all of which are being grown (at least experimentally) in either California or South Florida. We might as well admit right here that this legume grows better in California, with 12 inches of rain, than it does in Florida with 65. Yet it crops up everywhere; thousands of growers in both states are thrilled by the startling red flowers, and efforts to cultivate it are being intensified from year to year.

The chief species of *Erythrina* grown in the west are South African, because climatic conditions are similar. In Florida more attention is given to Indian, South American and tropical African species, perhaps on the theory that similar climatic conditions suggest more likely adaptability.

In any event, the various *Erythrina* trees and shrubs are exceedingly easy to grow; their chief drawback lies in the fact that various borers find the heartwood of most species highly delectable, and it takes all the poisons in the family medicine chest and infinite perseverance to prevent the borers from destroying their host. The best way to propagate *Erythrina* trees is from seed, if available, or from cuttings of any size up to fence posts. The best way to wipe out the borer is to cut off the branch tip he has already killed, ram a wire down the center of the wood till you feel a crunch, then seal the end of the twig with yellow laundry soap. Fortunately, many *Erythrina* trees, with age, seem to become immune to borer attacks, so it may correctly be said that the first ten years are the hardest.

Bailey's Encyclopedia summarizes the confusion over names thus: "The forms more or less in cultivation are likely to be imperfectly or doubtfully determined botanically." This is the under-statement of the year; it means that if you have a coral tree, it isn't the species you think it is. Perhaps a botanist can chuckle over your dilemma, but to laymen like you and me, this nomenclature is serious business. Therefore, the "Flowering Tree Man" who has seen and grown hundreds of *Erythrina* trees but knows nothing of their botany, will try to help other common folks separate the various species in our gardens.

The old spreading 30-foot trees you see in Coral Gables, Coconut Grove, in Bayfront Park in Miami, and elsewhere over South Florida, mostly are the Indian species *E. variegata*. There are, however, in the Miami area some big trees of the Peruvian species which grows to 80 feet, *E. micropteryx* (Syn. *E. poeppigiana*), the terminal leaflet five-and-a-half inches wide (twice as big as *E. variegata*); and there are specimens of the Panama tree *E. glauca* that grows to 60 feet, easily distinguished because its flowers are orange and the leaflets assume a vertical position in the evening.

Unfortunately, the Miami area does not possess this trio exclusively, because the following trees have been introduced and are grown sparingly: *E. grisebachi* (with double flowers); *E. berteroana* from Central America, perhaps

128. ERYTHRINA VARIEGATA

127. ERYTHRINA SENEGALENSIS

hardiest of the tree forms; *E. velutina* from Jamaica with vermilion corolla and chestnut-red wings, and *E. vespertilio* with very thin foliage and small leaves, an Australian giant which becomes 100 feet high in its native land.

That pretty well takes care of the trees that you are apt to see in your wanderings, although I have introduced *E. hondurensis, E. senegalensis, E. mulungu* and several other species, and isolated examples of these are to be found growing here and there in Florida.

Now to talk about the shrubs. The handsomest of them all when in bloom is *E. humeana* var. *raja* from South Africa. It is still rare in both Florida and California, becomes occasionally 10 feet, is spectacular in June with vermilion blossoms. Commonest of cultivated "corals" is the Brazilian *E. crista-galli* with velvety, dark crimson flowers mixed up with the leaves, a shrub sometimes six feet high and wide, often dying back to the ground in autumn and returning faithfully with spring. It is quite hardy and will survive as far north as Washington, D.C. I have seen it in tree form in Jacksonville eight feet high and with a four-inch-diameter trunk. It is closely allied to the frequently seen *E. falcata,* a six-foot Brazilian shrub which has no leaves mixed with the blossoms, and another Brazilian shrub, *E. reticulata,* which does better in low ground.

With the exceptions noted above, the flowers of all *Erythrina* trees growing in the United States are red. (A white-flowered sport of *E. variegata* has been introduced but has not flowered, so far as I know). Cold winters invariably make *Erythrina* blossoms a much more brilliant red; warm winters are followed by dull colorings.

The chief kinds of *Erythrina* trees cultivated in California, *E. caffra* and *E. speciosa,* are rare in Florida, though I am growing both in my garden in Stuart. Practically all *Erythrina* plants are prickly, although the Fairchild Tropical Garden, at Coconut Grove, distributed some thornless plants ten years ago from seed I furnished, but identity of the species and source of the seed got lost in one of our various Florida hurricanes.

If the foregoing discussion of the various kinds of *Erythrina* has not helped you understand the genus better, you might as well quit reading here. But for the sake of a few technically inclined individuals, I am reproducing, in over-simplified form, a key to the *Erythrina* trees cultivated in California, which was worked out some years ago by Elizabeth McClintock, of the California Academy of Sciences. Miss McClintock has done yeoman service in her efforts to clarify the nomenclature and separate the species; unfortunately, not all of our Florida-grown species are included in her key, but it is useful nonetheless. Her separation of species that bloom with or without the leaves does not hold good in Florida, probably because of excessive rainfall, but the idea is at least indicative.

Here is her outline, which starts with the length of the "banner," that is, the largest petal in the flower:
1. Banner 4 to 6 times longer than wide:
   A. Flowering before the leaves, *E. speciosa* and *E. coralloides.*
   B. Flowering with the leaves, *E. herbacea, E. americana, E. macrophylla.*
2. Banner 1⅓ to 3 times longer than wide:
   A. Calyx spathe-like:
      (1) Small deciduous trees, *E. latissima* and *E. variegata.*

129. ERYTHRINA SPECIOSA

130. ERYTHRINA HUMEANA

(2) Large evergreen trees, *E. caffra* and *E. lysistemon*.
B. Calyx entire, truncate or short-toothed at apex:
   (1) Banner 1½ to 2 times as long as keel:
      a. Inflorescence leafless, *E. falcata*.
      b. Inflorescence leafy, *E. crista-galli* and *E. x Bidwilli*.
   (2) Banner 2 times or more as long as keel:
      a. Shrubs: *E. acanthocarpa, E. zeyheri* and *E. humeana* var. *raja*.
      b. Trees: *E. humeana* and *E. arborescens*.

And now, one last word about our Florida native *Erythrina herbacea*, whose bright red spikes in the swamps along our roadsides and on the sandhills along the ocean are avidly gathered by garden clubbers for bouquets. It is a member of the same genus as these cultivated species we gardeners struggle with, though rarely is it dignified by being planted in anybody's garden.

Some years ago when the author was lecturing to a garden club in New Orleans and showing the members color slides of pretty trees that they could grow in that climate, he was besieged with requests for seeds of the "cry-baby tree."

This name apparently originated in New Orleans, because it was a complete mystery until a slide flashed on the screen of the red flower spikes of *Erythrina crista-galli*. "That's it!" screamed voices from all over the room, so now maybe we have a good common name for this handsome shrub or small tree. It does well in Florida, produces plenty of flowers and is cultivated in Jacksonville, Pensacola and elsewhere through the northern part of the state.

131. ONCOBA SPINOSA (Fried egg tree)

132. CLERODENDRUM MINAHASSAE

Oncoba—The "Chic" of Araby

Hundreds of wild white "roses" abloom on a single plant are the glory of a bushy Arabian tree being widely planted in the warmer parts of Florida and California. Its name—*Oncoba*—is, like the plant itself, of Arabic origin. The specific name of *spinosa* is in reference to the many sharp two-inch thorns in the leaf axils. The tree grows also in Nigeria, Kenya, Cameroons and Northern Rhodesia, often up to elevations of 4,000 feet.

Evergreen in favorable situations, *Oncoba* is deciduous when touched by temperatures near freezing. It withstands some cold but it is not hardy and does not survive the winters in north central Florida. Its dark green, cherry-like foliage, often a beautiful wine-red when young, contrasts sharply with the light gray bark of the trunk.

In April and May comes the abundance of solitary, white, scented flowers, three inches across, with numerous yellow stamens, not unlike large single white roses or camellias. In Nigeria, the tree is called the "wild white rose," though it belongs rather to the Flacourtia family and, among cultivated materials, has almost no relatives in the Temperate Zone.

The flowers, which grow in profusion along the leafy boughs, stem from the under side of the young branches and turn sunward to last only a day before the petals shatter. But new blossoms are always opening, and for a month or six weeks the succession of flowers on what is facetiously called "the fried egg tree," makes it a center of attraction in the garden.

The Division of Plant Exploration and Introduction of the United States Department of Agriculture has introduced *Oncoba spinosa* into this country and made it available to growers.

Oncoba blooms at 6 feet and rarely grows more than 10 feet high, although a veteran specimen in Palm Beach stands 20 feet high and measures as much in diameter. It also grows as a shrub, and as a bushy background plant it is exceptionally good in the large yard. Blossoms continue sporadically all through the year, though they are not to be compared with the over-all display of spring.

The fruits of *Oncoba* are smooth, 2½ inch spheres, flattened at top and bottom like those of the calamondin (*Citrus mitis*). They have very hard shells of a rich red-brown color, often with a sculptured surface or longitudinal rib-like markings and, in Africa, they are sometimes polished, hollowed out and used for snuff boxes, or sealed again with a few pebbles placed inside to become a child's rattle. The native name for *Oncoba* in the Gold Coast means "snuff-box tree."

Each fruit contains about fifty small seeds in a pulp which Macmillan says is considered edible, but famine must have been stalking the land when this report was made. Britton says the seeds contain chaulmoogric acid but this is flatly denied by Dalziel. The seeds do yield 37.6 percent of a drying oil suitable for paint but the difficulty of separating the small seeds from the pulp is an unfavorable factor.

133. LAGERSTROEMIA SPECIOSA (Queen's Crapemyrtle)

134. LAGERSTROEMIA TURBINATA

Lagerstroemia — the Tree Crapemyrtles

The common bush Crapemyrtle (*Lagerstroemia indica*) of southern gardens from Texas to North Carolina has many handsome tree relatives that are beginning to find a place as outstanding ornamentals in the warmer parts of Florida.

Of the perhaps 20 species of *Lagerstroemia,* 12 or more are Indian, 3 Malayan, and at least one Chinese—the common bush crapemyrtle of the South which despite its scientific name, *L. indica,* did not come from India. There are representatives of the genus also in Australia, Indo-China, New Guinea and Madagascar. The various species have many things in common: nearly all of them have showy mauve to pink flowers with wrinkled petals that would justify spelling the common name CREPE myrtle; their woody capsular fruits, seated on persistent woody calyces, contain many winged, usually small light seeds which are uncertain in their germinative power, a large proportion being as a rule infertile; their leaves have big pointed buds in the axils (a feature distinguishing the genus from *Eugenia* which it much resembles in habit); in many species the leaves wither red, which serves as an identifying note; the bark of most species flakes off in patches, rather like the Planetree (*Platanus*).

Commonest of the tree species in cultivation in Florida is the Queen's Crapemyrtle (*Lagerstroemia speciosa,* syn. *L. flos-regina*) which Macmillan calls "undoubtedly one of the most strikingly showy of flowering trees." Reaching maximum size in the damp jungles of Assam and Burma, Ceylon and Travancore, where annual rainfall is 180 inches or more, the *Jarul,* as the Hindus call it, becomes an 80-foot handsome timber tree, second in value only to the teak (*Tectona grandis*). It is found typically along river banks, but it is not confined to such places, and is plentiful, though in comparatively smaller size, in many parts of India where rainfall is as low as 50-60 inches. In this same rainfall bracket much of South Florida falls, and the Queen's Crapemyrtle makes itself very much at home. Shade the plant abhors, so that in the forest it grows fast and straight, reaching for the light. In the full sun of a Florida garden however it becomes a sprawling shrub of gigantic dimensions (sometimes 30 feet across), unless forced by staking to assume the responsibilities of a tree; as such it will reach 40 feet in 10 years. Because in its natural habitat the maximum shade temperature is 95-110°F., and the absolute minimum is 36-65°F., the Queen's Crapemyrtle is not found north of the Tampa-Daytona Beach frost line, though like some other plants it may adapt itself gradually to less protected areas, and become hardier when dormant. Ordinarily in South Florida it holds its leaves pretty well until February, coloring them bright red, and dropping them slowly in December and January. Once bare, it stays that way four to six weeks. However the blizzard of November 25th, 1950 that buried Ohio and Pennsylvania with record snowfall and extended its icy fingers into Florida, produced temperatures as low as 31°F. as far south as Miami. The *Lagerstroemia* trees in the author's yard at Stuart, Florida, were subjected to a 32° temperature for three hours on the morning of November 26th, but high winds prevented frost. Every leaf on *L. speciosa* curled up and dropped with the cold, and this year the tree will be bare several months.

The flowering period of *L. speciosa* extends over several weeks. It sometimes begins as early as May and occasionally lasts as late as August. Small plants in the sun may bloom when only 18 inches high. The inflorescence is an upstanding spike, far above the leaves, 3 to 4 inches in diameter, usually 8-12

135. LAGERSTROEMIA FLORIBUNDA

136. LAGERSTROEMIA THORELLII

inches, sometimes 18 inches long. The spike is massed with 3 inch flowers at its base where it begins to flower first and carries quantities of pink and green buds toward its tip. When first opening the rose-like scentless blossoms with 6 or 7 petals, are a rich, deep mauve, almost purple. They open full before sunup. On the first morning they have a fresh fluffy appearance from the projecting stamens. On the second they look weary, the stamens having coiled up in the night into a brownish mass in the center of the flowers, and during the day the petals fade to pale pink or white. Most of the flowers fall off by the third day, but the inflorescences are ample and flowering goes on for weeks. The color of the flowers varies with different trees; some being purple and others being different shades of mauve approaching pink. Occasionally a bright pink or a magenta is seen, and these are particularly beautiful, but the colors do not come true from seed. This and other species of *Lagerstroemia* can be grown from cuttings, but all of the plants seen in Florida are seedlings. Some trees bear quantities of seed, the pecan-size, green seed pods turning brown and persisting on the tree often into the next flowering season.

Florida growers get rich pleasure from the summer beauty of *L. speciosa,* but because it is bare for such a long period at the height of the winter tourist season, growers have looked favorably toward the introduction of other species which hold their foliage better, and one or two of which offer longer blossoming periods, reaching even into the winter tourist season.

One of these of great promise is the Malayan *L. floribunda,* shrubby in its Florida growth, although in Malaya it is a 60-foot, dense, bushy cone, its branches hidden by the foliage. This lovely tree was introduced here from India in 1934. For another picture and description, see National Horticultural Magazine, Oct. 1949, pp. 161-3. *L.*

floribunda is one of several species of this genus that are inclined to flower a second time in some years. The tree pictured in this article bloomed in June 1950, and it had a second flowering period the first week in November when it was as handsome as it was in early summer.

To the Harvard Botanical Garden in Soledad (Cienfuegos) Cuba goes credit for the introduction of two new evergreen species, *L. thorelli* and *L. turbinata*. There is a similarity between these two that suggests they may prove to be identical. Another species of doubtful validity, *L. thouarsi,* has been established in Florida from seed received by the author from India; this probably is identical with *L. thorelli*. Benthall in his "Trees of Calcutta" says *L. thorelli* is native of Cochin China and continues: "A medium-sized tree . . . flowers about $1\frac{1}{4}$ inch diameter, in copious axillary panicles; . . . This is a tree of moderate size with a short trunk . . . and pale yellowish-grey bark. . . . The flowers—in large, open clusters from near the bases of the leaves . . . are purple or lilac-coloured when they first open, but soon fade to an almost pure white. . . . This tree is not unlike *L. speciosa* . . . but has much smaller leaves and flowers; moreover, its flowers are less brilliant in colour even when they first open. . . . However, the tree does not compete with its more splendid relative because its flowers open after the break of the rains, when the *Jarul* flowers are over. . . . giving a fine display of bloom throughout the monsoon months. . . . This tree —is now common in gardens and is occasionally planted in streets as an avenue tree. . . . The leaves fall during the cold season and are replaced in February and March, the new foliage often being reddish in colour."

Ida Colthurst's "Familiar Flowering Trees in India" says of *L. thorelli:* "Being very popular for its beauty and long season of bloom, it is *le dernier cri* in tree planting." Lancaster: "An

137. LEUCADENDRON ARGENTEUM (Silver tree)

138. LAGERSTROEMIA INDICA (Bush Crapemyrtle)

Amateur in an Indian Garden" suggests that *L. thorelli* "which blooms later (than *L. speciosa*) will last from May to October and if spikes are removed as the flowers fall a second flush will result. This is an ideal amateur's tree."

L. turbinata blooms in Florida from August to November. Its much branched flower spikes above the foliage may be as much as 20 inches high and up to 10 inches wide at the base, carrying hundreds of blossoms. New flowers open bright mauve each morning, coloring gradually pink toward evening; next day they turn creamy-white and the third day brown before they fall off. In normal weather the flowering goes on for weeks. The tree grows tall, straight and slender; it is practically evergreen.

Among recent re-introductions is a doubtful species, *L. hirsuta*, which the United States Department of Agriculture brought in 30 years ago as P.I. 52512 with this memo: "A small tree with exceedingly ornamental flowers which are very large and purplish pink. It is found in the dry jungle of Korat." The tree is allied to *L. speciosa*. Although the U.S.D.A. had no record of the survival of any of these original trees, there is on the Van Dyck place in St. Petersburg, Fla., a large tree which seems to belong to this species and efforts are being made to identify it definitely. There is also a mature tree from the original introduction growing on the grounds of the Gorgas Hospital at Ancon, Canal Zone. From it a considerable number of trees have been propagated by the Canal Zone Experimental Gardens at Summit, C.Z., and distributed by them. Walter R. Lindsay, director, says of the specimen at Ancon: "The tree is approximately 75 feet tall with a spread of only 20 feet, although it is branched to within 10 feet of the ground. The base of the tree is 15 inches in diameter. The slender branches, one and a half to two inches in diameter, are drooping and show evidence of having flowered uniformly and profusely. The leaves are velvety and approximately three inches wide by seven inches long. The seed pods when dry are about three-eighths of an inch in diameter."

Through Mr. Lindsay the author obtained seed of *L. hirsuta*, propagated many trees and distributed them all over Florida.

It is noteworthy that the three hour exposure to a 32° temperature on November 26th, which stripped *L. speciosa* of its leaves, apparently failed to injure the foliage on five other species of tree Crapemyrtle in the same location. These were *L. thorelli*, *L. turbinata*, *L. thouarsi*, *L. hirsuta* and *L. floribunda*. All of these would seem to be hardier than the Queen's Crapemyrtle; yet no definite conclusion can be reached because all of the *Lagerstroemia* trees change their leaves at least once a year, and sometimes oftener. This leaf change is quick, so that the old foliage will be dropped in the course of a few days, and the new leaf growth will come on within a week. In effect many of the trees are evergreen.

The author has succeeded in establishing small trees of several other Crapemyrtles, notably *L. tomentosa*, which has handsome white flowers twice a year in great quantities. A particularly good lot of seed in the summer of 1950 produced a large crop of seedlings. Five previous plantings over 10 years failed to result in a single germination.

In West Palm Beach, Fla. on Parker Avenue near Okeechobee Road, is a specimen of *L. loudoni* which blooms infrequently. The flower spikes are 18-24 inches long and less than 3 inches diameter, individual blossoms are 1½-2 inches across, the coloring much like other species. Repeated efforts over many years have produced only one seedling from this tree, though seed is readily obtained.

173

The Queensland Umbrella Tree — *Brassaia actinophylla*

In a Florida garden stands an exceedingly handsome tree with glossy "tropical looking" foliage. It grew from seed and rose right straight up like a bean pole, up and up until it was nearly 25 feet high with no branches. True, it did have leaves all the way up the trunk, great big leaves two feet across, made up of 15 or 20 leaflets hung radially on the end of a 2-foot stem so that each leaf looked like an umbrella. These leaves are arranged symmetrically around the trunk to make a balanced green column.

For a costume ball one night the owner cut off the clustered leaflets just at the end of one of these stems, inverted this and wore it as a hat that won a prize.

Out in Queensland, Australia, where this tree is native, it is called umbrella tree (*Brassaia actinophylla*, syn. *Schefflera actinophylla*). The plant was introduced to the United States in 1927 by Frank Walsingham, and quickly became the most popular of pot plants.

The Florida specimen grew apace until a hurricane one summer day broke off the top half. This caused the stump to branch. The tree never had branches before and now it suddenly developed half a dozen. In the intervening years these have grown massive, and the original bean pole has become a lovely, spreading shade tree, incomparable for form.

When the tree was about 15 years old it began to bloom, which this species never does unless growing in full sun, but no one could predict when it would flower. One year blossoms came in March, another time in August, and on several occasions the tree flowered twice the same year. The small red blossoms clustered on great spikes 2 or 3 feet long, flow out the top of the trunk or main branches like so many ostrich plumes, and their intense color against a bright blue sky and offset by handsome foliage make a striking picture. Gradually the red flowers became red fruits over a period of six weeks or more, and these finally turn black, still soft and squashy like raisins but definitely ripe. The tree knows this too, but instead of shedding the individual fruits, it drops the long fruiting spikes and these shatter some as they clutter the ground around the mother tree. In every little fruit there are a dozen papery seeds, not yet ready until the pods are thoroughly dry.

Now to reveal a trade secret! The seedpod branches are gathered and laid on cardboard on the floor of the garage. Then the clustered pods are pulled off, packed in a box, and mailed to a florist in Switzerland—of all places! He shells out the seeds, plants them, and year after year he produces 10,000 plants from seed grown in Florida on an Australian tree! What does he want with them? He sells them for house and patio plants, to be grown in tubs or pots, and they do marvelously well in this capacity.

Here is a subtropical plant of great merit that can be grown indoors in the temperate zone, in pots, tubs or shuberies, in patios or conservatories, anywhere the temperature does not go below 18° F, because the umbrella tree is used to extremes of warm and cool weather. By growers all over the United States it is considered the most satisfactory plant ever introduced from abroad for ornamental planting, because it can be used many different ways. Even in Florida it is found growing against foundations and in corners, producing its array of handsome foliage, dark green and shining. It appears in window boxes, tubs, and patios. When it starts to get big it can always be dug up and moved outdoors. A look of consternation always crosses the faces of Florida visitors when they look at a huge umbrella tree and suddenly realize that this is the "shrub" a high-priced landscaper planted in a spot by a picture window back home.

After the tree develops big branches after the top is broken out, each branch suddenly starts to develop auxillary (adventitious) roots. These roots emerge several feet up from the base on side branches 6 to 8 inches from the main trunk. Roots come out from every direction. If allowed to grow these auxillary roots will take hold in the ground if they have opportunity. These roots may circle the tree trunk and try to choke the parent. These adventitious roots can be cut away, but on occasion a limb having bunches of roots near the union with the trunk is cut off and planted to produce another tree. This phenomenon of developing auxillary roots probably would never happen in plants grown in containers.

The umbrella tree is a good example of a tropical tree that sometimes begins its life as an epiphyte or as an "airplant." If one of the seeds is dropped by a bird into a crotch of a nearby tree and finds moisture and accumulated debris to nurture it, germination takes place and an umbrella tree begins to grow. As the young tree grows, its roots will grow down the trunk of the host tree until they reach the ground. As soon as the roots reach the ground, the umbrella tree begins to grow in earnest. It drops more roots, and these will gradually encircle the "host" tree and choke it to death. The umbrella tree that began as an air plant will become the giant of the forest, and the tree that mothered it as a baby will die and rot away.

139. BRASSAIA ACTINOPHYLLA (Schefflera or Umbrella tree)

175

140. SYZYGIUM MALACCENSE (Malay apple)

141. SYZYGIUM MALACCENSE

The Cultivated Eugenias in American Gardens

Eugenia was once considered the largest genus of trees and shrubs in the world, comprising more than two thousand species of myrtaceous evergreens in the tropics. Most of the standard reference books in print still cling to this genus as a catch-all, but its complexities have induced taxonomists in recent years to break it into two main groups, plus a score or more smaller genera. Broadly speaking, the genus *Eugenia* is now understood to include most of the New World species, and the genus *Syzygium* comprises most of the Old World plants, with a few of these allocated to *Acmena* or *Cleistocalyx*.

This split was suggested by Merrill and Perry twenty years ago and is now generally accepted, but unfortunately horticulturists have been slow to pick up such switches in nomenclature and have a tendency to cling to *Eugenia* as a generic name for all the plants of the group. In this they are abetted by some of the not-too-modern reference books. They are encouraged too by publications like M. R. Henderson's revision of "The Genus *Eugenia* in Malaya" in which all genera kept separate by Merrill & Perry, and by Bailey, are thrown back into *Eugenia*. They are confused when outstanding botanists like Bullock and Harrison, in a recent issue of the Kew Bulletin, refuse to accept *Syzygium* as generically distinct from *Eugenia*.

It is a troublesome group of plants, and the existing confusion is increased by the fact that there continue to be a few "true Eugenias" in the Old World (their special floral arrangements agree with New World species rather than *Syzygium*, etc.) and also because many species are still imperfectly known or as one botanist wrote, "they are separable with difficulty or uncertainty."

Consequently, horticulturists in the United States, are looking forward with keen anticipation to the forthcoming *Hortus III* with a revision to date of accepted nomenclature for the everyday gardener.

In the proposed edition of *Hortus*, these species of *Syzygium* are recognized:

aromaticum	jambos
buxifolium	malaccense
cumini	oblatum
grande	pycnanthum

and these species of *Eugenia* are accepted:

alternifolia	longipes
axillaris	mato
brasiliensis	monticola
buxifolia	natilitia
condensata	oblanceolata
confusa	paniculata
coronata	pitanga
currani	polycephaloides
cyanocarpa	pungens
eucalyptoides	rubicunda
klotzschiana	simpsoni
ligustrina	uniflora
luschnathiana	uvalha

The editors of *Hortus III*, however, warn that although these species of *Syzygium* and *Eugenia* are thus listed in the manuscript for the revised edition, they feel free to make changes before publication if they see fit.

The author hopes they amend their lists, because 12 of the species named are not in cultivation in the United States; at one time they may have been, certainly a few were introduced by the USDA but failed to become established. And, on the other hand, several Florida natives and half-a-dozen species grown comercially in Florida and California are not listed in *Hortus III*. (The species *S. buxifolium* and *E. buxifolia* are not synonyms—they are different plants, and the latter is confusing because according to the Index Kewensis, four quite different plants scattered over the world have been described by different botanists and called *Eugenia buxifolia*.)

We, in the Temperate Zone, have only one basic contact with the Eugenias—this is through the spice we call cloves, which are the dried flower buds of a Moluccan species. It has never been

The author acknowledges his indebtedness to R. Bruce Ledin, George H. M. Lawrence, Julia Morton, D. J. McSwiney, George W. Kosel, Jr., Nixon Smiley and last but not least Paul Root of Cam-Art Studios, who died during the course of photographing *Eugenia* species for this article.

142. SYZYGIUM JAMBOS (Rose apple)

143. SYZYGIUM SAMARANGENSE (Java apple)

established in cultivation in this country.

But many Eugenias bear delightful, edible fruits and millions of people living in warm countries are very familiar with plants quite unknown to us. In fact, except for fewer than a dozen species indigenous to South Florida, the genus is almost entirely tropical. The greatest concentration of species is in Malaysia, (North Borneo alone has 150 species of *Syzygium*) and some parts of Brazil, although Cuba with 125 species, Australia with perhaps 50, Central America and Mexico with 50 or more, Africa with probably 40, indicate the pantropic spread. [There are no Eugenias in Europe.]

E. J. H. Corner served twelve years at the Botanic Garden in Singapore and made special study of *Eugenia* in that hotbed of species. He wrote:

"*Eugenia* is one of those big groups of tropical plants to which there is no introduction in general botany and which discover themselves as a new idea when we approach the study of a tropical flora.

"Except the dwarfed and shrubby treelets of mountain tops, the Malayan Eugenias are trees of considerable size. Unfortunately it is not possible to distinguish most kinds by a short description, though they may be recognized at a glance, for where one may seem distinctive there are always several related to it and differing only in details of flower, fruit, leaf-shape, or veins of the leaf, and as there has been much error in identification it is not yet certain which are really common. Still, it is easy to recognize a *Eugenia* by its simple, opposite, leathery, shortly-stalked leaves that generally point down and have upcurled sides, from the absence of stipules (so that there is no line or scar connecting the stalks of a pair of leaves across the twig, as there is in the Mangrove and Ixora families), from the clusters of white (or pink) fluffy and sickly sweet flowers and the inferior ovary which ripens into a berry with 1-2 large seeds, but has no stone.

"Malayan Eugenias are evergreen, shedding their leaves gradually through-out the year, but new leaves and flowers they develop at seasonal intervals. Some flowe once a year after pronounced dry weath , most seem to flower twice a year after each dry spell; and not a few flower three or more times. Of these last, the Sea Apple (*S. grande*) is the best example. In the south of the Peninsula where it is a common roadside tree, it flowers about the middle of March to the middle of April, from the end of July to the middle of August and about the end of December to the middle of January. Sometimes it has small flowerings, too, about the middle of June, the end of September and the end of November. As the flowering is gregarious, many trees being affected at the same time over a wide area, it must be a climatic phenomenon that is dependent, perhaps, on some alternation of dry and wet, or hot and cool, weather too subtle to be detected by ordinary meterological records. Some years, the trees flower earlier or later than is their wont, exactly as the change of the monsoon is unpredictable, and some flowerings are poor: indeed, two good flowerings are seldom consecutive. The March flowering is the most regular and, generally, the most striking. Every tree will then flower for 10-20 days, although the height of flowering, when the crown is whitened as with snow, lasts in each case only 4-5 days or a week. The fruits take a little over 2 months to ripen, which is the same for clove-fruits. Unfortunately, we have no exact records for other species, not even for the fruit trees, but we are certain that among the other species there are very marked differences that are worth investigating."

The few Eugenias that are distinguished as pretty flowering trees, are from the Old World (Malaysia). The fruits of a few Old World species are attractive to the eye but most insipid to the taste, or at least of doubtful interest. Contrariwise, many of the New World species bear delightful edible fruits that are in great demand where available. But the flowers of the New World plants are not pretty and draw no special interest.

So much for an introduction to the complexities of this group with a thousand children, whose peculiarities are

179

145. EUGENIA CURRANII

144. SYZYGIUM MALACCENSE

difficult to separate because often not well defined, whose behavior is different in different environments and whose possibilities have only been sketchily investigated. A starting point for our discussion can at least be made from the species actually in cultivation in Florida or southern California. Separating these into Old World (*Syzygium,* etc.) and New World (*Eugenia,* etc.) groups makes the relationships easier to understand. Nomenclature is based on Bailey's *Manual of Cultivated Plants* and the manuscript of *Hortus III* with synonyms given for the convenience of interested persons.

Old World Species

Syzygium jambos (L.) Alston. Rose Apple.

(Syn. *Eugenia jambos* L.; *Caryophyllus jambos* Stokes; *Eugenia malaccensis* Blanco but not L.; *Jambosa vulgaris* DC; *Jambosa jambos* Millsp.)

This dense evergreen Malayan shade tree of 30 or rarely 40 feet high, and trunk diameter of 15 to 18 inches, has spread to every warm country in the world and reproduces so prolifically that in some areas it threatens to become a pest. Yet it is much cultivated for its handsome form, bushy spreading top, rose-fragrant 3-inch greenish-white "powderpuff" flowers and attractive 2-inch fruits that really smell and taste like a rose.

The flowers in March and April in Florida, lasting only a few days, are quickly followed by quantities of fruits, each containing 1 (rarely 2) seeds that rattle around in the yellow to pinkish-white fruits. One reason the Rose Apple spreads so rapidly is that the seeds are polyembryonic (like those of the mango) and one seed frequently produces 3 to 8 plants. The flesh of the fruit is dry and crisp. It is not particularly good eating, rather insipid with a rose-water flavor, but candied, preserved or made into jelly, it is highly prized as a delicacy. The ripe fruit is so pretty it is often used for table decoration.

The Rose Apple is much planted in Florida where it seems to thrive on poor soil and neglect. It has been found useful too for its resistance to salt spray. The fruits are not sold in Florida markets as they are in Malaya.

Syzygium aqueum Alston. Water Rose Apple.

(Syn. *Eugenia aquea* Burm.)

Burkill reports this is "a small, crooked fruit tree, wild in southern India and eastern Malaysia, cultivated widely in southeastern Asia for the sake of its slightly aromatic, white or rose-pink fruits, which are eaten to relieve thirst." He explains the fruit is like that of the common Rose Apple (*Syzygium jambos*) except it is less elongated and lacks the rose flavor.

Wm. F. Whitman of the Rare Fruit Council (Miami) is growing a Taiwan (Formosa) marcot of this tree at Miami Beach but it has not fruited yet.

Syzygium pycnanthum Merrill & Perry. Wild Rose Apple.

(Syn. *Eugenia densiflora* (Blume) Duthie.)

A Malayan slender evergreen tree to 30 feet with oblong leaves 4 to 10 inches long and 3 inches wide, superficially similar to those of *Syzygium malaccense* and *E. currani.* Occasionally the tree develops a bushy crown and massive trunk. Corner says this and its variety *angustifolia* are among "the most beautiful flowering Eugenias." The blossoms are white or pink or clear rose-colored, each 1½ to 2 inches wide, clustered in dense 6-inch heads in the leaf axils. *E. densiflora* var. *angustifolia* has quite dissimilar, long, narrow leaves, usually 1x6 inches or larger. The flowers are smaller than the type, white or cream colored, very fragrant, and the 30-foot bushy tree is whitened when in flower. The variety sustained less damage than did the type by 30 degree temperatures in Florida in January 1958. The round black fruits are about ½ inch in diameter. This is commonly called the River Rose Apple.

Syzygium grand~ Wall. Sea Apple.

(Syn. *Eugenia grandis* Wight.)

A very large evergreen Malayan tree, in its native land reaching 80 feet in the open, and 100 feet or more in the coastal forest canopy. It develops a dense, heavy crown with massive wide-spread limbs.

The glossy leaves, up to 9 inches long and 5 inches wide, with a distinctly down-turned tip, are thickly set on the branches which seem to droop with the weight of foliage.

David Fairchild in 1926 brought the first seed to Florida from Singapore and some of the original introductions are now big trees in the old Miami City Cemetery. Because it grows fast and because the thick bark is fire-resistant, the trees have long been planted as avenues in Malaya where they are uninjured by grass fires.

The 1-1½" white, fluffy ball flowers with a strong, rather sickly fragrance, come in dense clusters to 6 inches wide, and the tree with its glittering green foliage, when covered with a heavy mantle of white flowers, is very showy. The natural range extends to northern Australia.

The fruits ½x1", oblong, have a green leath-

147. EUGENIA LUSCHNATHIANA (Pitomba)

146. EUGENIA AROMATICA (Clove)

ery rind when ripe, dry but edible.

A common name for it in Australia is White Apple.

Syzygium malaccense (L.) Storr. Malay Apple.

(Syn. *Eugenia malaccensis* L.; *Syzygium malaccense* (L.) Merr. and Perry; *Eugenia bauaguica* Blanco; *Jambosa malaccensis* DC.)

One of the world tropics' most beautiful flowering trees, this dense evergreen from Malaya reaching 30 to 40 feet, bears magenta or red-purple brushes that come bursting very abundantly from trunk and branches on short stems. These are succeeded by crimson-colored, egg shaped fruits 2 to 3 inches long which have a soft, juicy, edible pulp.

Neal: *In Gardens of Hawaii* writes: "The tree is very handsome. Smooth, mottled gray bark clothes the trunk and the foliage consists of dark-green, shiny, oval leaves. In March and April when flowering, a grove of mountain apples is especially beautiful. As the cerise pom-pons fall a bright red carpet is laid on the ground below. The trees grow rapidly, prefer moisture to dryness." They are recommended as a windbreak.

The fruit is either white splashed or striped with pink or wholly crimson to purplish, and slightly shiny, and contains 1 or sometimes 2 seeds; Quisumbing reports that in the Philippines it is sometimes seedless. Some varieties of the fruit have a pleasant flavor but mostly the taste is insipid. Freeman & Williams (Trinidad) suggest that "stewed with sugar and some flavoring, e.g. cloves, they are a moderate substitute for pears."

The flowers of the Malay Apple are seen at their best only when one is standing directly under the tree, wrote David Fairchild, "at which time they appear to form a fairy haze of enchanting loveliness." "For a perfect blaze of color, nothing exceeds the Malaya apple in flower," wrote Burkill.

In Hawaii this tree is called *Ohia ai,* (ai means edible) to distinguish it from *Ohia Chua* (*Metrosideros polymorpha* and relatives) and *Ohia ha* (other species of *Eugenia*). Another common name is Pomerac.

One reason the Malay Apple is not better known in South Florida is that it is quite sensitive to frost damage. An 8-foot tree in my garden at Stuart was hard hit by 30 degree temperature in December 1957, losing all leaves. New growth started within two weeks, and when this was an inch long, further 30 degree weather struck, killing the whole top of the tree except one branch which is now recovering.

Syzygium samarangense (Blume) Merr & Perry. Java Apple.

(Syn. *Eugenia javanica* Lam.; *Eugenia alba* Roxb.)

A Malayan tree of 20 to 30 feet, its evergreen leaves 4-10x2-3½" rounded at the base, blunt at the tip. The flowers 1-1½" wide, white, from the leafy twigs, much less conspicuous than those of *S. jambos,* are followed by waxy, green or whitish, pear-shaped fruits, few to many, 1-1½" long by 2-2½" wide, or larger.

Except for flower and fruit colors, the tree much resembles *S. malaccense.*

Benthall says the tree is unusually handsome and is much planted in India for ornament, rather than for its fruits which are almost tasteless and not much eaten except by poor people. In the Philippines, Brown "Useful Plants of the Philippines" says the fruits are pink; he calls the tree "very pretty, top shaped."

Syzygium cumini (L.) Skeels. Java Plum.

(Syn. *Eugenia jambolana* Lam.; *Myrtus cumini* L.; *Syzygium jambolana* DC.; *Eugenia djouat* Perr.; *Calyptranthes jambolana* Willd.; *Eugenia cuminii* (L.) Druce.: *Eugenia cumini* Merr.)

The extensive synonymy shown here might well be explained by the exceedingly complex behavior of this big East Indian tree, sometimes to 50 feet, with smooth, glossy, somewhat leathery, evergreen leaves, 3 to 15 inches long and 1 to 3 inches wide, which are a lighter green below than above. The tree grows naturally from India to the Philippines and Hawaii and has been extensively planted in other warm lands, including Florida and southern California, chiefly for shade but also because it is highly wind-resistant.

The confusing variation in Jambolan trees begins with the leaves. In Malaya, Corner found two distinct kinds; in the south end of the peninsula the leaves are 2-5x1-2" and the small flower clusters 1-2½" long; in the north around Penang the trees have leaves so large (6" or more) they are hard to tell from *Syzygium grande* and the flower clusters are 2-4" long.

In Malaya the fruit is ¾-1" long, oblong, deep purple to black, juicy, with one green seed. In Florida the fruits are somewhat larger up to 1½" long, dark maroon or purple in color, more or less the size and shape of an olive. There is wide variation in fruit taste and desirability.

Watt's *Dictionary of the Economic Products of India,* reported: "It is chiefly found along river beds and is specially cultivated for its fruit in gardens and in avenues. There are several varieties that yield much better flavored fruit than others, but as a rule it is astringent, and only serviceable when cooked."

Popenoe: *Manual of Tropical and Sub-Tropical Fruits* reflects this with his observation: "It is said that forms with large fruits of good

183

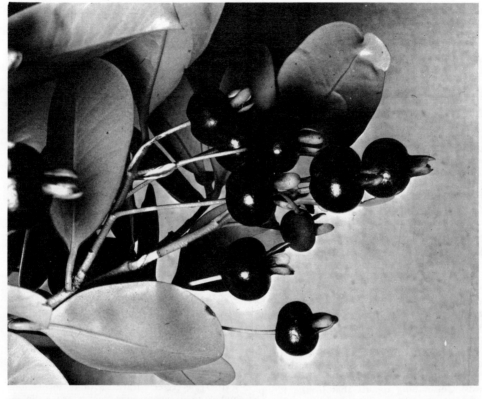

149. EUGENIA BRASILIENSIS (Grumichama)

148. EUGENIA AGGREGATA
(Kiaersk, Cherry of Rio Grande)

quality are known in the Orient, but those which have been grown in the United States are scarcely worth cultivating." It should be noted that Popenoe was writing of varieties with fruits only ½ inch long.

Quisumbing calls the fruits growing in the Philippines "luscious, fleshy and edible."

Burkill quoted K. Heyne as enumerating several races of Jambolan in Java, including one that is seedless. Burkill adds: "Improved races may bear fruits as large as pigeon's eggs, and one exists in the Philippine Islands which may bear seedless but small fruits."

Miller, Bazore & Bartow: *Fruits of Hawaii* discuss this variation: "There are at least two varieties in Hawaii, one with small somewhat irregular-shaped fruit and one with slightly larger symmetrical olive-shaped fruit. The smaller variety has purple flesh and the larger type has whitish flesh. Some trees produce better quality fruit, both in size and flavor, than others. The white-fleshed Java plum is sweeter and less astringent than the purple-fleshed variety. . . .

"The Java plum tree . . . produces a large quantity of fruit which fall to the ground and stain everything with which they come in contact. It is often considered an undesirable tree in Hawaiian gardens and along roadways and streets because of the unsightly litter produced beneath the trees.

"Birds have scattered the seeds far and wide. . . .

"Because of their astringent qualities, fresh fruits of both the purple- and white-fleshed varieties pucker the mouth and are undesirable to eat out of hand . . . The purple-fleshed fruits contain little or no pectin. In contrast, the white-fleshed Java plum contains relatively large amounts of pectin."

Alex Korsakoff with an exceptional opportunity to observe two Java plum trees in the old Miami City Cemetery where he has been superintendent more than 30 years, pursues the subject of variability. He keeps his trees separate by calling one "cumini" and the other "Jambolana." He writes:

"If you want *jambolana* plums, you can have some right now (October) with viability guaranteed. If you want *cumini* plums, you will have to wait till early next summer. My taste preference as fresh fruit is *cumini*, as to the jelly—*jambolana*.

"The trees are different, the leaves, the flowers and the fruit are different, though all these things resemble one another very, very much. Time of flowering is also different. All my years in Miami I never saw more than one crop of *Syzygium cumini*, while *Eugenia jambolana* has sometimes as many as three crops during the late spring, summer and early fall period. While *E. jambolana* is almost constantly covered with scale, *S. cumini* is clean."

The flowers of the Java plum are numerous, scented, pink or nearly white, without stalks, and borne in crowded clusters from the axils of fallen leaves on old wood near the branch tips. The petals cohere and fall all together as a small disc. The stamens are very numerous. Chittenden in error calls the flowers red.

The bark of the Java plum tree is smooth, light gray with broad patches of darker color. Fruit is also called Jambolan or Jambolan Plum.

Eugenia currani C. B. Rob.

This attractive Philippine shade tree, sometimes to 30 feet, has a gnarled trunk, tortuous branches and quadrangulate young growth. It is rare in cultivation in Florida, represented only by specimens in special collections, possibly because viable seeds are not available.

Young and older twigs are conspicuously 4-angled or winged as the leaves are decurrent. Leaves opposite, simple, entire, or undulate, very short petioled; blade large, to 6 inches or more, sometimes to 12 inches long, and 2¾ inches wide, thick and leathery, mostly obovate or oblanceolate, apex bluntly acuminate, base cordate, glabrous, midvein prominent and yellow, lateral veins also prominent. New leaves a beautiful bright red color.

Flowers begin to appear 2 to 3 months before they open, gradually increasing in size. The inflorescence is a tight branching cyme or panicle, 2 to 4 inches long and up to 4 inches in diameter, the flowers produced tightly together on the branches among the leaves. Flowers ⅝ inch wide; calyx of 4 or 5 small sepals, papery, often rose-tinged. Petals pinkish, 4 or 5, overlapping and they fall off in one piece, so they are cup-like and do not unfold; stamens numerous, white, erect, to 1⅝ inch long; sepals, petals, and stamens borne on the thick rim or edge of the cup or hypanthium. Ovary is embedded at the base of the cup; style white, elongated but shorter than the stamens.

The fruit is a berry, nearly sessile, produced 20 to 50 in a tight cluster, each fruit the size of a small grape, to 1½ in. wide, globose, apex crowned with calyx ring and small sepal points, at first white, then gradually turning pink, red, and then dark purple-red or almost black. The fruit clusters, up to 3 inches long and 2½ inches wide, are on the bare branches or between the leaves on the more mature twigs. The flesh is red near the skin, otherwise white, rather dry and crisp, and pronouncedly acid with a pleasant flavor not unlike that of a crab apple. The flowers on the tree appear in May or June and the fruit ripens in July or August. The relatively large seed which clings to the flesh is sometimes absent. The fruit from the trees at the Sub-Tropical Experiment Station at Homestead, Florida, is seedless. The fruit is too acid for use as a dessert, but would in all prob-

150. EUGENIA GRANDIS (Sea apple)

151. SYZYGIUM GUINEENSE

ability make an excellent jelly and is used in the Philippines for making preserves, wine and pickles. The 20-year-old trees at Homestead are only 20 feet high. In some years the leaves are attacked by red spider, causing defoliation. A Philippine farm journal says the tree is of "vigorous growth, succeeds well where the wet and dry seasons are strongly accentuated, and requires well-drained land for the best results. In productiveness it is apparently exceeded by no other species of the genus."

Acmena smithi (Poir.) Merr. & L. M. Perry. Lilly Pilly.

Eugenia smithi Poir. *Syzygium smithi* (Poir.) Niedenzu; *S. brachynemum* F. v. M.; *Acmena floribunda* var. 2 DC).

An evergreen Australian tree found near water courses, occasionally to 30 feet but more often a tall shrub or bushy tree of half that height. The ovate or lanceolate leaves are 2 to 3 inches long. T.N.R. Lothian, director of the Adelaide Botanical Garden writes: "It is freely grown here, particularly in coastal districts, as it may be touched by frosts further inland. In summer the snow-white clusters of fringed flowers are quite showy, and are followed, maturing in winter, by great masses of berries, ¼ to ½ inch diameter, varying in color from lightest to deepest mauve-purple. They are edible, incidentally, but few know it among those of **mischievous age.** Lilly Pilly forms a magnificent windbreak hedge."

Ernest E. Lord of Melbourne writes: **"The** bloom does not last long but the berries remain for 6 months; highly ornamental."

Eugenia paniculata Banks. Brush Cherry.

(Syn. E. *myrtifolia* Sims not of Roxburgh. *E. paniculata* Banks & Sol. var. *australis* Wendl.; *E. australis* Wendl.; *Syzygium paniculatum* Gaertn. l. c.; *Myrtus paniculata* J. F. Gmel.; *Jambosa australis* DC.; *J. thozetiana* F. v. M.)

The correct name of this Australian evergreen tree has been much discussed by botanists. Undoubtedly there is wide variation in the species. Not only are the leaves attractive, glossy, bronze when young, but the flowers are striking, fluffy, pure white, in summer, and the oval deep red berries of good size, hang on all fall and winter. It is a cone-shaped tree to 50 feet, holding its foliage to the ground, often growing near water courses. Kajewski in northern Queensland found the white flowers "very showy." In California this tree is much planted for accent and for wind screens. Its columnar form is very effective on the landscape.

Half a century ago the Reasoner brothers at Oneco, Florida introduced what botanists call a horticultural form of this Australian tree under the unpublished name *Eugenia hookeriana* and

they used it for windbreaks and salt-resistant hedges. It is still occasionally seen in south Florida, but because it acts as a host to white fly and is usually covered with sooty mold, careful nurserymen avoid its use. In appearance it much resembles *E. paniculata* but it is not so bushy, not as handsome, does not prune as well. The rose-purple fruits are much larger than those of *E. paniculata* and are often used in Florida for making jelly. *E. paniculata* does not seem to attract sooty mold.

Two distinct dwarf forms of *E. paniculata* have been developed in California. One is reported to be a hybrid. For all practical purposes it is a small-leafed, compact edition of *E. paniculata,* and is much used for tubs, pot plants, etc. The other takes a stumpy, pyramidal character, small leaves, distinctly reddish-brown tinted, with definite decorative attributes where a dwarf is needed. This plant is used to excellent advantage in Disneyland miniature settings to simulate full-grown trees at about 1/10 scale.

Eugenia cyanocarpa F. Muell. Blue Lilly-Pilly.

This lovely shrub or sometimes a small tree to 12 or 15 feet, has a semi-drooping habit not unlike a weeping birch. The elliptic, slender-pointed leaves are 2 to 4 inches long. The creamy white flowers, quite inconspicuous, are followed by loose clusters of round fruits ½-inch in diameter that are a beautiful metallic blue in color and most attractive. This plant has been sparingly cultivated in California for many years but is not offered in the trade.

Eugenia coronata Schum. and Thorn. Utowana.

This shrub, native to West Tropical Africa, was introduced in 1932 by David Fairchild of the USDA under (P. I. 73117). It is an attractive, slow-growing evergreen to 10 or 12 feet high that could be used for foundation planting, though it is not known to be carried in the nursery trade. It forms a thick, dense, compact growth.

Bark rough, grayish-brown. Leaves opposite, simple, thick and leathery, dark green above, pale below, resembling privet. Petiole short, thick and cord-like, often curved. Blade to 2 inches long and 1¼ inch wide, oval or oval-elliptic, obtuse, entire, veins obscure. Lower surface of blade glandular dotted.

Flowers white, 1 to 3 together, in axils of leaves, ½ to ¾ inch diameter; calyx of 4 sepals, pale green, resin dotted, obtuse, to ⅛ inch long, cap-like. Petals 4, spreading or in some forms cup-like, white, obtuse, to 1 inch long. Stamens

152. EUGENIA MYRTOIDES

153. EUGENIA MYRTIFOLIA (Brush cherry)

numerous, not longer than the petals. Two very small persistant bracts at base of each flower. Sepals, petals, and stamens borne on a cup or hypanthium, the ovary inferior. Fruit solitary on short stalks to ⅜ inch long; odd-shaped, mainly elliptical, but also obovate or oval to ⅝ inch long and ⅜ inch wide, with 4 small, pointed sepals at apex; when mature dark purplish-black; flesh juicy, purplish-black. One large seed, oval in shape, to ⅜ inch long or less.

The inconspicuous flowers are produced off and on all year except in December and January, and the fruit matures in 3 to 4 weeks. It is edible but not especially desirable. Some forms of this shrub in cultivation are more vigorous and should be selected for propagation. Some forms have flowers that do not expand and the pistil is abortive so no fruit is produced.

New World Species

The New World species of Eugenia are just as numerous—probably a thousand of them—and just as confusing, or more so, than their Old World relatives. Something new is added here, however, for among the New World species are many that bear luscious and delightful fruits, and palate appeal always takes precedence over beauty or utility.

Brazil is particularly rich in these edible numbers, and their botanists, breaking away from *Eugenia,* have created a host of new genera, including *Abbevillea, Campomanesia, Stenocalyx, Calyptranthus, Aulomyrcia, Phyllocalyx, Gomidesia, Rubachia, Marlierea, Britoa, Myrciaria,* etc. Some of these have not yet been widely accepted. Insofar as the following species are listed in the forthcoming *Hortus III,* the author sticks to that classification of them, and gives the accepted synonyms. However, this author hopes that the compilers of *Hortus III* will give this exceedingly difficult family a lot more study in an effort to reconcile conflicts herein with the book in its preliminary form. Certainly species not cultivated should be eliminated, and species that are in cultivation should be included if the book is to have its maximum usefulness to the layman.

This author omits the genus *Cleistocalyx,* which appears in *Hortus III,* because it is not encountered in cultivation. He includes the new genus *Myr-*

ceugenia because one very beautiful flowering tree in that genus has appeared on the American landscape. Several plants grown in the United States and formerly classed as Eugenias, are now referred to *Myrtus, Myrcia* and other genera and have been omitted here.

Eugenia eucalyptoides F. Muell.

This tree with rather large white flowers in sparse compact terminal clusters, is native of Northern Queensland. It was introduced in Florida 50 years ago by the USDA as P.I. 36043. It is a dense, bushy tree with landscaping possibilities, holding its evergreen foliage clear to the ground, but it is not widely cultivated in Florida.

West Indian and South American Species
Eugenia aggregata (Vellozo) Kiaersk. Cherry of the Rio Grande.

This native of Brazil was introduced to Florida and California in 1938 under the erroneous name of *Myrciaria edulis* (Vell.) Skeels, and still is offered by some nurseries in California under this name. It is a handsome ornamental shrub or small tree, evergreen and somewhat slow growing, useful for landscaping but not well known. It is cold hardy and can take temperatures to 24 degrees F.

Generally it is a shrub or small tree to 15 feet with bark green and pale orange, peeling or shedding in thin layers. Leaves glabrous, thick, short petioled, narrow elliptic, apex obtuse, base acute, dark shining green, entire but somewhat revolute, veins obscure, petiole grooved, blade to 3 inches long and ¾ inch wide. Young new leaves may be silky tomentose.

The flowers are solitary but borne in pairs opposite each other in the axil of a bract at the base of new growth. Flowers on one-inch stalks. Two conspicuous leafy, heart-shaped or ovate bracts are borne below each flower, not united but overlapping and clasping pedicel. Sepals 4, spreading flat, narrow, slightly constricted at base. Petals 4, white, alternating with sepals, recurved back, to ½ inch long. Stamens numerous, to ⅜ inch long, erect in center of flower, borne on edge of disk. Ovary inferior, style one, green, slender, as long as stamens.

The fruit is a berry, oblong or obovate, to one inch long and ¾ inch wide, turning orange-red and then deep purple-red when fully ripe. Skin thin; flesh pale orange, juicy, of good flavor, slightly sub-acid. Seeds absent in some fruits, others with one or two large white seeds to ⅜ inch long, round, but flat on sides adjacent to each other. The ovate bracts persist at base of fruit and the 4 sepals persist on top of fruit. Fruit edible and can be used for making a pie. The fruit has a cherry-like flavor.

154. EUGENIA DOMBEYII (Grumixameira)

155. MYRCIARIA FLORIBUNDA (Rum berry)

Flowering takes place in March, April or early May and the fruit is ripe in about 3 weeks.

The plant is well adapted to the rocky alkaline soils of Dade County, Florida, and does well in acid sand. It should be grown more.

Nomenclature here is extra confusing. The Brazilian tree above described is not listed in *Hortus III*, but that reference book does list another *E. aggregata* as a synonym for *E. condensata* Baker, a Madagascar tree which, so far as this author can determine, is not in cultivation in the United States.

Because of the complications, Dr. R. Bruce Ledin of the University of Florida's Subtropical Experiment Station at Homestead, has given me this story of the Brazilian *E. aggregata:*

"In 1938 William H. Ott of Whittier, California, obtained seeds of a plant labeled *Myrciaria edulis,* the 'Cambuca' of Brazil. He was corresponding with Dr. H. S. Wolfe, then in charge of the Station here, and told him that in São Paulo this plant is called 'Rio Grande Cherry.' He sent Dr. Wolfe two seedlings and he planted them out in the arboretum September 22, 1938. In 1941 they fruited and have done so nearly every year since then. The Station has distributed a number of seedlings over the years as *Myrciaria edulis,* and since 1955, as *Eugenia aggregata.* It makes a very handsome evergreen shrub or small tree which in some years (April and May) fruits very heavily. The fruit is edible and actually quite good, except it does not have an awful lot of flavor—I like *Eugenia luschnathiana* better. The plant is quite cold hardy.

"This plant has been offered to the trade by Mr. Ott, and also the Armstrong Nursery in Ontario, California, has offered it for sale. It is listed, described, and illustrated in their 1952 catalogue, page 99, as *Myrciaria edulis,* the Cherry of the Rio Grande: 'We think this is one of the finest new subtropical fruits to be introduced to California.'

"I have never been satisfied that this plant was properly identified and I am certain that it is not in the genus *Myrciaria,* for according to Bailey's Manual, the hypanthium tube is prolonged beyond the inferior ovary, as in *M. cauliflora,* in which a small ring of calyx tissue is present on top of the fruit—this is not present in our plant. So our plant is not a *Myrciaria* and it is not *Eugenia edulis.*

"In the spring of 1955 I sent flowering material and a photograph of the fruit to Dr. Richard Howard at the Atkins Garden of Harvard. He replied:

" 'The herbarium specimen of the unknown Myrt. arrived safely and we are pleased to have the material. As you are well aware, the American *Myrtaceae* is in a horrible shape, but I think I have the answer for you on this particular plant. It is neither *Myrciaria edulis* nor *Myrcianthes edulis,* but appears to belong in a small section of *Eugenia.* The specimen you sent compares favorably with the type of *Phyllocalyx cerasiflorus* described by Berg. This section was established on the basis of the large involucral bracts which subtend the flower and fruit. This genus must now be recognized as a section of *Eugenia.* However, the name *"cerasiflorus"* is preoccupied and the next available name apparently is *E. aggregata* (Vellozo) Kiaersk. The species is based on a specimen collected by Sellow in Minas Geraes in Brazil. We have a duplicate of the type as well as a photograph of the type from the Paris Herbarium. There seems to be little doubt that this is the correct identification. I showed your material to a visiting botanist from Colombia who is also quite an expert on the flora of Peru and he reports that they have the same material in cultivation and unidentified. He has checked over our work on this particular specimen and agrees that *E. aggregata* is the most appropriate name for this material at the present time.' "

Eugenia atropunctata Steud.

This shrub or small tree to 18 feet from Dutch Guiana has inconspicuous white flowers and bears tiny black fruits of no value. In manner of growth and general appearance the tree resembles *Syzygium jambolana* except that the leaves are much smaller. It was introduced by the USDA as P. I. 221180 but has not been widely distributed.

Eugenia brasiliensis Lamarck.
Grumichama or Grumixama.

(Syn. *Eugenia dombeyi* (Sprengel) Skeels; *Myrtus dombeyi* Sprengel).

Although a tall Brazilian tree, this was first introduced in 1911 as P.I. 30040 from Mauritius where it was described as a very fine shrub, 10-18 feet with glazed leaves and white blossoms.

Considerably cultivated in southern Brazil for its delightful fruits that look like oversize gooseberries and taste somewhat like huckleberries, the *Grumixameira* (the suffix—*eira* in Brazil refers to the tree rather than the fruit) divides into several races, white-fruited, red-fruited, and deep violet-fruited.

Dr. Wilson Popenoe introduced this tree again in 1914 as P.I. 36968 and wrote of it:

"Both as a handsome ornamental tree, and for its pleasantly flavored, cherrylike fruits, the grumichama deserves to be planted in gardens and dooryards throughout the Tropics. It has not yet become well known outside its native country, Brazil, though it is cultivated in numerous Hawaiian gardens, and even in as remote a part of the world as Mauritius.

"The tree, which grows to 25 or 35 feet, is shapely and densely clothed with deep glossy

147. EUGENIA LUSCHNATHIANA (Pitomba)

146. EUGENIA AROMATICA (Clove)

a year. The Surinam cherry is rare in California, although it is cold resistant to 20° and is prized for oceanfront planting because of its resistance to salt spray.

The cherries are first green, then yellow, orange and finally a deep crimson. They should never be eaten till fully ripe when they drop off the bush at the touch of a finger, for immature fruits are resinous and pungent. When ripe they have a delightful aromatic, distinctive flavor. When a newcomer first tastes a Surinam cherry, he often finds it disagreeable. But oldtimers like nothing better than a handful to eat.

Eugenia uniflora has several common names. Where "Surinam" came from is uncertain because the plant did not originate in Dutch Guiana. In Brazil the fruit is called Pitanga (which should not be confused with another species *Eugenia pitanga* Kiaersk., a low shrub, all young parts covered with reddish down. This is not in cultivation here). Another common name is Brazil Cherry.

The Surinam Cherry is believed to be the only *Eugenia* fruit that is offered for sale in Florida markets.

Myrceugenia apiculata (DC.) Niedenzu. Temu.

(Syn. *Eugenia apiculata* DC.; *Eugenia luma* Berg.; *Myrtus luma* Molina but not of other authors.)

Hortus III describes this as a shrub or small tree of 6 to 30 feet, bark becoming golden brown, flaky. Leaves ½ to 1 inch long, ovate to oblong, sharply apiculate. Flowers cream-white becoming suffused coral red, about ½ inch across, cymes long-peduncled, petals 4, calyx lobes 4, rounded. Fruit black. October. Chile. Inhabits moist shaded areas. Useful in subtropical areas as landscape plant, windbreak, or for hedges. Withstands full sun.

This tree was brought into cultivation some years ago by the California State & County Arboretum at Arcadia. Under the names *Myrtus apiculata* and *Myrtus luma*, it has been cultivated in England for a hundred years and is prized for its profuse flowering. Over there it is sometimes confused with *M. lechleriana*, a very similar Chilean plant. Both are commonly called "tree myrtle."

Myrciaria cauliflora Berg. Jaboticaba.

(Syn. *Eugenia cauliflora* DC.)

This name has been confused in the literature. Actually there are three different, but closely allied trees in Brazil with similar fruits that are known collectively as Jaboticaba. For an explanation of distinguishing features of *Myrciaria*

cauliflora Berg., *M. jaboticaba* Berg. and *M. trunciflora* Berg. see Hoehne's book on Brazilian fruits. Incidentally, the Brazilians put major emphasis on the first syllable, then run the other syllables together fast with only a minor accent on "cab"—JAB'-ot-i-CAB'-a.

These evergreen trees to 35 feet, upward branching from near the ground, bear clusters of short-pediceled white flowers with conspicuous stamens, produced directly from trunk and branches. These are followed by thick-skinned, grape-like fruits that are 1 to 1½ inches diameter, the pulp a pleasing vinous flavor suggestive of the muscadine grape. Each fruit contains 1 to 4 oval seeds.

Christian Halbinger Frank, Mexico City, who has been growing Jaboticaba there, writes: "M. jaboticaba takes 5 years until fruiting and M. cauliflora 30 years, but M. cauliflora has better fruit. Grafted trees from the M. cauliflora tree on the estate of S. W. Younghans, 1020 N.W. 49th Street, Miami, are the best to bear consistently in this area so far."

Harry Blossfeld, São Paulo, Brazil, plantsman, writes of these trees:

"Some 200 miles west of São Paulo is a city named Jaboticabal which got its name from the fruit tree. In that city there are thousands of trees in all back yards and orchards. People stream to the city at harvest time and orchard owners charge an entrance fee for which you can pluck as many fruits as you can eat. Or they charge another fee for each five gallon can you take out with fruit. Jaboticaba jelly is most popular with us and any suburban piece of land offered for sale is charged an additional price for each Jaboticaba tree standing on it. Jaboticaba trees are practically the only trees ever transplanted in a big size with root ball; with this one exception, nobody would have care for buying a grown-up tree and pay for its hauling. It takes from 12 to 15 years to get a plant from seed into first fruiting, but by grafting on a more vigorous variety here known as 'Paulista' it is possible to get young trees to bear fruit three years after grafting, or six years after sowing the stock."

Paulo Nogueira-Neto from São Paulo, Brazil says: "Our jaboticaba trees are now severely attacked by a fungus. It is a great problem. The fruits are covered by the yellow spores of the fungus and also the leaves are attacked."

Myrciaria edulis (Vell.) Skeels.

Hortus III describes this: "Tree to 20 feet; brs. pendant lvs. 2.3 in. long, willow-like and rusty-pubescent when young: fls. ½ in. across axillary or terminal in clusters; fr. about 2 in. long, pear-shaped, downy, ill-smelling, orange-yellow. February. Brazil." The same reference

193

156. EUGENIA CORONATA (Utowana)

157. EUGENIA SIMPSONII

book gives *Eugenia edulis* Vell. as a synonym.

Confusion begins here because the tree being grown in Florida under the name *Eugenia edulis* Vell. definitely is not in the genus *Myriciaria*, and consequently cannot be *Myriciaria edulis*. Here is Dr. Bruce Ledin's description of the tree cultivated in Florida:

"This native of Brazil is an evergreen shrub or small tree with an open, scraggly type of growth. Branches tend to be at right angles to the stem and this accounts for the open growth. New leaves and branches are soft white pubescent but mature growth is glabrous.

"Leaves willow like, opposite, simple, set rather far apart, short petioled; blade small and narrow, to 3 inches long and ¾ inch wide, but mostly 2 to 2½ inches long and ⅝ inch wide, or smaller, becoming thick and leathery, acute, lanceolate to elliptic-lanceolate or almost linear, midrib prominent but lateral veins somewhat obscure and few in number (5 to 6 pairs).

"Flowers solitary in axils of leaves on new growth, about one inch across, with 5 recurved pointed hairy sepals, 5 white petals, and many prominent stamens.

"Fruit large, to 2 or 2½ inches in diameter, globose, covered with a fine pubescence ("downy"), pale yellow-green, edible but not desirable as it has a very pronounced odor and flavor suggesting garlic.

"This is not a handsome plant and the fruit is not especially desirable; grown mostly as an oddity. Originally offered to the trade by Reasoner's Nursery in Oneco, Fla., many years ago."

Confusion increases as we review the description of *Eugenia edulis* which appears in Peter Riedel's (California) book "Plants for Extra-Tropical Regions." He wrote:

"A small willow-like tree from the river Plata in Brazil. There are still a few specimens in Santa Barbara, survivors of those Dr. Franceschi grew. The best one is in Dr. Franceschi's old nursery, just above Franceschi Park, a specimen 18 foot tall, with a very graceful habit, pretty at all times but a spectacle when yellow with fruit which, in some seasons completely obscures the foliage. It varies in size both large and small fruits being found on the same branch, but an average sample weighed 3 ounces, was 2½ inches in diameter with a circumference of 7½ inches. This fruit is delicious, the shape of an apple or peach and somewhat downy and yellow. In a good year, the ground under the bush is so thickly covered with fallen fruit that one may not step there without crushing one or more of them. It will never be a good shipping fruit because it is soft and the skin is thin and easily broken but, if it were much better known, no home orchard would be without it. This small bush, in certain seasons bears over 2000 fruits

but, in other years, may have but a few. It grows where it gets no cultivation at all and only the water resulting from the usual rainfall. Seedlings in pots have given some difficulty; they do not like having their roots confined; once planted out, they seem healthy enough, though the growth, at first, is slow and the plants do not seem to bear until they are 8 or 10 years old."

Obviously, Riedel was not writing about the tree which California nurserymen call *Myriciaria edulis* but which in this article is called *Eugenia aggregata*. (q.v.) When Riedel's description was called to Dr. Ledin's attention, he wrote:

"My description of *Eugenia edulis* nearly fits Riedel's. If the plants are the same, and I think they are, I do not see how Riedel can say that 'the fruit is delicious'—our fruit has a decided garlic odor and taste and is very acid—maybe there are some good forms of it? Our fruit is yellow and is downy and the size of a peach. It definitely is not in the genus *Myriciaria*, so it can't be *M. edulis* according to *Hortus III*. Popenoe has a brief description of *Eugenia tomentosa*, page 310, and it is also mentioned on page 282 of the Proceedings of the Florida State Hort. Soc. for 1958 as the cabelluda, *Eugenia tomentosa*. These fruits came from our tree here which we have labeled as *E. tomentosa* but which appear to be *E. edulis*. Chapman Field distributed plants of *E. edulis* (*E. tomentosa?*) in 1951 (P.I. 161873) as *E. sp.*, which we have here, and the Atkins Botanical Garden in Cuba sent us seeds of *E. uvalha* in 1952 which have fruited here and they appear to be *E. edulis* (*E. tomentosa?*) which fits Riedel's description except that the fruit is not 'delicious.'

"So we have a problem here in identifying the true *E. edulis* and *E. tomentosa.*"

Unfortunately, *Hortus III* is no help. It does not list *E. tomentosa* at all, although it does describe *E. uvalha* to the extent: "fruits round or oblate, yellow at maturity, aromatic."

The confusion may be summarized thus: The *Eugenia edulis* trees growing in Florida and California are definitely not in the genus *Myriciaria*. The plant called *Myriciaria edulis* by California nurserymen is definitely *Eugenia aggregata*. If the plant called *Myriciaria edulis* in *Hortus III* is in cultivation in the United States, this author does not know where. (See description of *Eugenia tomentosa* earlier in this article).

Myrciaria floribunda (West) Berg.
Guava or Rum Berry.

(Syn. *Eugenia floribunda* West.)

Native to the West Indies (Cuba, Hispaniola, Jamaica, Puerto Rico, Virgin Islands, Lesser Antilles, and northern South America). In St. Croix the aromatic balsam-flavored berry is used for preserves and put in rum for flavoring. The

158. EUGENIA UNIFLORA (Surinam cherry)

159. EUGENIA UNIFLORA

fruit makes excellent jam with an aromatic flavor.

The plant was distributed by the USDA in 1932 but probably was offered by the Royal Palm Nursery at Oneco, Florida, many years ago. It is not well known in cultivation.

Handsome shrub or tree to 30 feet, but in Florida to only 15 feet high, forming a thick dense growth. Bark guava-like, mottled, and peeling in thin flakes. Leaves opposite, simple, entire, glabrous, with obscure glands, short petiole; margins tend to be revolute; blade lanceolate to ovate-lanceolate, tapering on upper part to a long narrow point; lateral veins obscure; 2-3 inches long and $\frac{5}{16}$ inch wide.

Flowers white, $\frac{3}{8}$ inch diameter, nearly sessile, borne profusely, often one flush after another as in coffee, in clusters of 4 to 6, in axils of leaves. Calyx of 4 minute sepals represented only as mere points; petals 4, white, very small; stamens numerous, white, conspicuous, borne with the sepals and petals on upper rim or edge of cup or hypanthium; ovary half inferior, not joined to hypanthium, rather seated at its base; style longer than the stamens.

Fruit borne solitary, near ends of twigs, globular, short-stalked, with 2 small bracts at base, $\frac{1}{2}$ inch long. In the yellow form the surface is resinous dotted and the flesh translucent showing the many veins. Besides the yellow fruited form just mentioned, another type has dark-purple-red fruit, almost black, like the color of jaboticaba, the veins and dots obscured because of the dark pigment; this black type tastes better as it is not so resinous. Seeds one, large, dark colored, kidney shaped and filling most of the fruit so flesh is scanty.

Flowers produced May to July, usually in June, with sometimes a second flowering in September. Fruit is ripe from August to October, with the September bloom maturing fruit in November and December.

O. W. Barrett, in "The Tropical Crops" says: "The guava-berry, *E. floribunda*, of the Virgin Islands and Puerto Rico, has long been known for its dark red or blackish fruits of the size of a small cherry. The intense balsam-like aroma of the purplish pulp is hardly equaled by any other fruit; it is used in making jams, and formerly a heavy liqueur and a strong wine, very popular in Denmark and the neighboring countries, were exported from St. Thomas in large quantities. There are three or four varieties in the dry hills of St. Croix; these vary as to size and color, but all are intensely aromatic. Unfortunately this excellent fruit does not take kindly to cultivation."

Pimenta dioica Merr. Allspice.

(Syn. *Pimenta officinalis* Lindl.; *Eugenia pimenta* DC.)

Native to Jamaica, Cuba, Mexico, and Central America. Wood, leaves, flowers, and unripe fruit all very aromatic. Tree said to become 30 to 40 feet high in Jamaica, but usually 10 to 15 feet in Florida. Bark pale brown and mottled, peeling in flakes. Young stems conspicuously 4 angled or square. Leaves opposite, simple, petioled ($\frac{5}{8}$ inch); blade thick and papery or leathery, dark green above, pale below, glabrous, with many glandular dots on both surfaces, margins entire but undulate and revolute, apex obtuse, elliptic to elliptic-oblong or oval-oblong in shape, mid vein impressed above but more prominent and becoming yellowish below, lateral veins not many but conspicuous, blade to 6 inches long and $2\frac{1}{2}$ inches wide.

Inflorescence short, to 3 inches long, borne in axils of leaves on new growth, a many branched cyme, the branches in 3's. Flowers small, $\frac{1}{4}$ inch across; sepals 4 minute; petals 4, white; stamens many.

Fruit a berry, small, $\frac{1}{4}$ inch diameter, globose, conspicuously glandular-dotted with green, becoming dark-purple-black when ripe, pulpy, sweet but almost tasteless, with 4 small sharp sepals as a crown on top of fruit, 1 or 2 seeded.

This is a handsome, evergreen, ornamental tree with upright growth, attractive bark, and dense, dark green foliage. Flowers in spring and fruit ripe in early summer. It does well in alkaline mucky soil and is recommended for planting as an ornamental. It can be propagated by cuttings or seeds. The leaves both fresh and dried have a very strong, spicy agreeable odor.

The allspice of commerce (often called "Jamaica pepper"), is made from the berries which are gathered when still green but full grown and dried in the sun. The tree is not planted commercially in Jamaica but fruit is picked from wild trees or those that were left when the area was cleared. It is used locally and exported for use in cookery for flavoring, and in medicine as a stimulant, and is said to be smoked like tobacco in some places in Mexico. Oil of pimenta made from the ripe fruit is used also in medicine and in perfumery. The allspice of commerce is so named for it has the flavor of cloves, cinnamon, and nutmeg.

Eugenias Indigenous to Florida

Nine species of *Eugenia* are native to Florida, but some are so seldom cultivated or even seen that few residents of the State are aware of their existence. A few agencies have tried to grow and popularize the best of them; outstanding in this effort are Simpson Garden Center, Woodlawn Park Cemetery, Fairchild Tropical Garden, all of Miami, as well as

161. MYRCIARIA CAULIFLORA (Jaboticaba)

160. SYZYGIUM CUMINI (Java plum)

the City of Miami Parks Department.

In contrast to the rare appearance of a native *Eugenia* in anybody's garden, introduced species are planted everywhere in South Florida, almost to the point where it might be said that at least one kind can be found in everybody's garden. They seem to be very much at home in this climate and adapt themselves to landscaping uses.

Several of the Florida species are found also in the West Indies. Contrariwise, a few West Indian natives are found in Florida but have probably been introduced. As Cuba is a hotbed of *Eugenia* species, it seems strange that so few of these have ever reached the United States.

Herewith are brief descriptions of the nine native Florida species:

Eugenia anthera Small. Small's Eugenia.
Farrar's "Guide to Southern Trees" says:

"This is a small tree or large shrub found in hammocks along the coast of southern peninsular Florida. It may be distinguished by its very small leaves, ½" to 2" long, and dark-red or black fruits. It is of no commercial value."

Small says the bark is pale, rather smooth; the leaf blades slightly paler beneath than above, the corolla slightly longer than wide. He adds that the brown heart-wood is close grained and hard.

Eugenia axillaris (SW.) Willd.
White Stopper.
(Syn. *Myrtus axillaris* SW.)

A small, slender tree of 20 to 25 feet, common in hammocks all over south Florida, often shrubby along the upper East Coast. Walter M. Buswell in his "Native Trees and Palms of South Florida" says of it:

"Flowers axillary, white, fragrant, often so dense they form a continuous cluster along the branches, calyx with pale hairs on the outer surface.

"Fruit reddish-purple, turning black, 7-12 mm. long, usually wider than long, juicy reddish-purple flesh. Often with a few or many woody galls in place of the fruit, and occasionally all the fruits replaced by galls. These galls are found on other *Eugenia* but never as abundant as on this species.

"This tree gives off a skunk-like odor that is noticed for a considerable distance and one can always be certain that the plants are somewhere in the vicinity. The odor is more noticeable from a distance than when close up; crushed leaves often have a slight odor, but not always. The flowers are fragrant; green fruits have an aromatic odor."

The leathery evergreen leaves 1-3" x ½-1" are mostly oval or elliptic, dull dark green above, minute black dots below. The stout petioles, sometimes winged, are purple.

Eugenia bahamensis Kiaerskou.
Bahama Eugenia.
(Syn. *Anamomis bahamensis* (Kiaerskou) Britton; *Mosiera bahamensis* (Kiaerskou) Small.)

West says this native of the Florida Keys and the Everglades Keys bears nearly stalkless flower clusters, seedy fruits and upright branches.

Eugenia buxifolia (SW.) Willd.
Box-Leaf Eugenia.
(Syn. *Eugenia myrtoides* Poir.; *Myrtus buxifolia* Sw. This is not the *E. buxifolia* of other authors.)

This West Indian tree becomes shrubby in Florida where it grows all along the east coast from Cape Canaveral to Key West. The bark is light brown, roughened by old leaf bases.

The shrub has very small elliptic or oval leaves, usually ½ to 2 inches long that are close set on the branches, resulting in a dense crown with lots of fine black dots on the lower surface of the leaves, though these are not always noticeable. The small white flowers are in short clusters on bare parts of the branch or on short leafy spurs. The oval or nearly round, black, aromatic fruit contains one pale brown seed. The heavy crops of berries are an abundant source of food for birds. The shrub is common on cut-over land, and West reports it is the dominant plant on some of the Florida Keys.

Other common names are Spanish Stopper and Gurgeon Stopper.

A different plant with tiny, gray-green leaves called "*Eugenia buxifolia*" and occasionally seen in Florida gardens, may be *E. buxifolia* Phil. from Chile.

Eugenia confusa DC. Redberry Eugenia.
(Syn. *E. garberi* Sarg.).

Sargent reported this (70 years ago) as the largest myrtaceous tree in North America, reaching a height of 50 or 60 feet, with a trunk 18 to 20 inches in diameter, and called it "one of the most beautiful of Florida trees." No one of the present generation has seen trees so large; mostly they are 30-45 feet, the branches slanting upward to form a narrow, compact crown. Buswell in 1945 reported many trees in Brickell Hammock, Miami, and some on Key Largo. Nixon Smiley (1958) found a group of trees on the north side of the intersection of U.S. Highway No. 1 and S. Miami Avenue. Unfortunately, most of the Redberry Eugenias have been bulldozed from the mainland so that they have become rare, and unless brought back for use in ornamental horticulture, they may soon be extinct in South Florida. The species has been reported in the Bahamas and in some of the

163. EUGENIA CONFUSA (Red Berry Eugenia)

162. EUGENIA AXILLARIS (White stopper)

West Indian islands.

Eugenia confusa is the only large native tree in the genus. Leaves on old specimens are small, ovate or narrow elliptic with a long, pointed, acuminate tip, bright glossy green, 3-5 cm. long, according to Buswell; but on young trees the leaves are larger, ovate or nearly orbicular with a long, acuminate tip, small dark spots on both sides of the leaf, 4-8 cm. long. New leaves are pale red.

The minute white flowers in dense axillary clusters in autumn, are followed by round scarlet fruits 10-13 mm. diameter.

The bark is ordinarily smooth, gray; but on older trees narrow strips of partly loose bark hang down.

Many old-timers in Florida refer to the tree as Red Stopper, but this common name is sometimes applied to other species as well. Sometimes this tree is called Ironwood, which makes for confusion because Ironwood is a "common name" for scores of different trees, including the following which grow in Florida: *Krugiodendron ferreum, Ostrya virginiana,* three different species of *Cyrilla, Cliftonia monophylla, Exothea paniculata,* and *Bumelia lyvoides.*

Eugenia dicrana Berg.
Twinberry Eugenia.

(Syn. *Anamomis dicrana* (Berg.) Britton; *Anamomis dichotoma* (Poir.) Sarg.) .

Allied to Simpson's Stopper, this is a smaller tree 25 to 35 feet, with loose reddish bark, often in shreds. It is recognized readily by 3-flowered clusters of white, fragrant flowers in the leaf axils, followed by nearly round, reddish brown, aromatic fruits, 6-7 mm. diameter. The flower stems are longer than the leaves so that when the tree is in bloom, the numerous white stamens stand out beyond the foliage.

The tree is found abundantly in some hammocks from Cape Canaveral south to Key West, but strangely enough is missing in others.

Other common names are Twinberry Nakewood and Naked Stopper.

Eugenia longipes Berg.
Trailing Eugenia.

(Syn. *Mosiera longipes* (Berg) Small) .

Ordinarily a shrub to 3 feet with slender erect branches, but occasionally a small tree. It is found chiefly on the Keys, especially on Big Pine Key.

The oval or ovate leaves are conspicuously reticulate, glossy above, and have dark red veins beneath.

The tiny white flowers, dense bunches of white stamens resembling guava flowers, are often abundant and Buswell called them "very showy." The fruit is dark purple or black.

Eugenia rhombea (Berg.) Krug & Urb.
Spiceberry Eugenia.

This small tree occurs in Florida only in hammocks in the southern tip of the State and on the lower Keys to Key West.

The olive green leaves with conspicuous black dots on them, are ovate, tapering gradually to a narrow, round tip. They are from 1 to 2 inches long.

The white flowers, about 1/3 inch wide, are in few-flowered clusters in the axils. These are followed by nearly globular 1/2-inch fruits that are orange and red, turning black, the skin somewhat roughened by glands.

This species also is sometimes called Red Stopper.

At one time this species was referred to *Eugenia procera* (SW.) Poir., a West Indian species, and Nehrling in "My Garden in Florida" wrote of it:

"This also is a very handsome Eugenia with fine dense evergreen foliage. The berries are orange, tinged with red, and black at maturity. Fruits picked in their orange color supplied seeds that germinated without difficulty. These Eugenias ought to be largely propagated and used as ornamentals. All of them make fine, dense small trees when given sufficient room to develop. None of them do well in dry soil. Hammock soil, consisting mainly of rotted old leaves, is what they require."

Erdman West, author of "Native Trees of Florida" reports that he has never seen this species growing in Florida.

Eugenia simpsonii (Small) Sarg.
Simpson's Eugenia.

(Syn. *Anamomis Simpsonii* Small) .

A dense strongly buttressed, upright evergreen tree to 50-65 feet that grows sparingly in some of the hammocks north of Miami, and one of the handsomest of Florida trees. Unfortunately it is rare both in the wild and in cultivation. It is distinguished by leathery leaves, elliptic, oval or abovate, bright green and shining on the upper side; the tip acute or round and notched, black dots above and below, 2-7 cm. long. The spicy-fragrant white flowers in forked clusters of 3 to 15, on long slender peduncles, are made up of a dense mass of stamens with fine thread-like white filaments and tiny, globular pale yellow anthers. The edible, round or oval, aromatic red fruits, 12-15 mm. diameter, are hunted by birds. The thin, smooth, creamy or pale reddish-brown bark flakes off, exposing fresh, lighter colored bark and giving the trunk a mottled appearance, not unlike the related common guava (*Psidium guajava*). *Eugenia simpsoni* is sometimes known as Simpson's Stopper or as Simpson Nakedwood. Its specific name honors Charles Torrey Simpson, pioneer botanist of the South Florida wilderness.

Small says the foliage contains a volatile oil, somewhat resembling that of nutmeg in flavor.

201

164. BAUHINIA CUMANENSIS (Turtle vine)

165. BAUHINIA CANDIDA

Bauhinia — The So-Called Orchid Trees *

Most popular of flowering tropical trees from southern California to Florida[3] and in restricted warm areas of the Gulf Coast are the so-called "orchid trees," which are not orchids at all, but belong to the bean family. Many of them do have pretty flowers, remotely orchid-like in appearance, which are responsible for the common name. The correct name of the genus is Bauhinia, honoring botanists John and Caspar Bauhin who were not twins, as sometimes reported; John was born in 1541 and died in 1631, Caspar was born in 1560 (19 years younger) and died in 1624. The dual brother idea is carried out by the plants, for practically all of the 500 kinds[4] of *Bauhinia* have two-lobed or twin leaves, shaped to suggest the imprint of the cloven hoof of certain animals, and this resemblance has given to the plants, in many countries, the common names of cow-hoof, bull-hoof, horse-hoof, goat-hoof, sheep-hoof, camel-foot, deer-hoof, mule-hoof, etc.

Actually, the leaf shapes of *Bauhinia* vary considerably and are of three distinct types: (a) Simple leaf which is notched, cleft, incised, or divided to some degree, thus making a bi-lobed leaf. This division may merely be a slight indentation at the apex (as in *B. retusa*) or it may be to the middle of the leaf or nearly to the base (*B. rufescens*). The common species in cultivation are of this type— but it is the "twin lobes" of the leaf not "twin leaves." (b) A few species (apparently none in cultivation) have entire leaves with an obtuse or pointed apex and resemble the common red-bud leaves. (c) Some species, especially those of Australia, have the leaf completely divided to the base to form two distinct leaflets, as in *B. hookeri*. Here, then, the leaves are "twins."

Not all the *Bauhinia* are trees; many are shrubs, vines or even gigantic lianas with stems curiously shaped, flattened or corrugated and twisted owing to a peculiar mode of growth in thickness.

Unfortunately, there is considerable confusion in the identity of many of the *Bauhinia* trees being cultivated in this country, which is only made worse by some of the available reference books. Part of the confusion arises from the fact that seedlings frequently do not produce flowers the same color as found on the parent tree. More trouble arises from the ignorance of writers who never tried growing anything but who become enthusiastic in print about flowering trees; one recent book with some claim to scientific endorsement ran a color plate of a *Bauhinia* flower with the wrong botanical name on it. Add to these difficulties the fact that seed often comes into the United States from a foreign country under the wrong name, sometimes the result of carelessness but often an honest mistake, and this mis-naming persists for years till the plant grows and flowers and can be re-identified by someone who knows his *Bauhinia*.

---

[3] *B. variegata* has been grown successfully as far north as Ocala. Also plants have been tried in Gainesville and Daytona Beach but a cold winter will usually kill them back to the ground. In Gainesville, one small tree flowered in January but it was killed later that year. The tree prefers warm areas, but it has succeeded as far north as New Orleans where it has survived temperatures down to twenty-six degrees Fahrenheit. *B. saigonensis* has been grown successfully under slat shade in Gainesville.

[4] We are aware that most books say there are about 250 species of *Bauhinia*. But after checking through Kew Index and all the available floras of tropical countries, we have come to the conclusion that the number of species is probably close to 500. Of these, probably about fifty are in cultivation throughout the world, but only about ten species are well known. There are more than a hundred species native to Brazil.

* Written in collaboration with Dr. R. Bruce Ledin, University of Florida, Homestead, Fla.

167. BAUHINIA SAIGONENSIS (Saigon orchid)

166. BAUHINIA VAHLII (Malu creeper)

Under the circumstances, the only way to begin to understand the *Bauhinia* that are in cultivation is to describe and picture these plants in the field. The authors have all the species herein described growing in Florida. They have consulted with other growers and botanists with wide experience in Florida, California, Australia and elsewhere. The separation of species as herein set forth, therefore, accords with the appearance, growth habits and other characteristics of the actual plants, even though in some instances these do not agree with some scientific authorities.

The Big Three

Most widely known among these attractive trees available to the grower is an Indian tree, *B. variegata*, variously known in the United States as Florida orchid, Poor Man's orchid, or Mountain Ebony. It is a medium-sized tree with stocky trunk, stiff branches and thick foliage. The smooth, dark green leaves, four to six inches broad, are heart shaped, the lobes rounded at the bottom, but the species is difficult to identify by leaf shape, as will be explained later.

B. variegata might well be called the "winter-spring-blooming orchid tree" because it flowers from January to March, and this would help distinguish it from two other common trees (next described) which are very similar in foliage. Sometimes *B. variegata,* especially small trees, will bloom as early as December, and in central Florida the flowering often continues into April. The blooming proceeds while the leaves are falling from the trees or, in the event of a cold spell or prolonged drought, after the leaves have all fallen. This is when the plants are the showiest—no leaves on the tree and in full bloom. The conspicuous flowers at the branch tips are mostly a vivid purple with broad petals, but mixed with the purple are heavy streaks of red and white in the same flower. The color of the

flower of *B. variegata* does not vary nearly so much as in *B. purpurea* (next described). The typical form comes out reddish purple, some trees with flowers more red (magenta) than purple, and the color gradually fades to a bluish-purple (mauve), giving rise to the name "Blue orchid trees" by some. There is some variation in the red color of the fresh flowers—it may be purple-red, pale purple, lavender, or almost a pale lavender-red resembling a peach flower from a distance. There are no all-red flowers in this species. One particularly beautiful form is pure white and this is correctly known as *B. variegata* var. *candida*.

Frequently confused with the foregoing, even by experts, is another Indian tree, *B. purpurea,* taller, not so stiff, very bushy, with flowers appearing at least three months ahead of *B. variegata*. It might well be called the "fall-blooming orchid tree" for in some years the blossoms appear as early as September, though normally they flower from October to December. Unlike the foregoing tree, *B. purpurea* blooms when the leaves are still on the tree. The spidery flowers of *B. purpurea,* appearing in big clusters at the branch tips, are usually lavender, but the color and size of the flowers are extremely variable. There are no true white forms of this species that we have ever seen (*B. alba* refers to *B. variegata* var. *candida*). The color range is from an almost near white but tinged with pink, through shades of pink, rose-red, old rose, carmine, dark purple,· lavender, violet, fuchsia. *Bauhinia purpurea* var. *violacea* (not *B. violacea*) suggests the reddish-violet color, variety *rosea* the rose form. 'Bonnie Red' is the one with deep carmine-colored petals. 'Simpson's Pink' is the best of all the *B. purpurea;* it makes a large, spreading, handsome shade tree and flowers in great profusion from early October to December. The flowers are larger than the other types and are a beautiful shade of rose pink. It comes true to type when grown from seed if not

169. BAUHINIA GALPINI (Red orchid)

168. BAUHINIA TOMENTOSA (St. Thomas tree)

crossed up with any other type of *B. purpurea* growing near by. *B. triandra* is a synonym of *B. purpurea* and should not be used to refer to any variety.

The form of the flowers of *B. purpurea* is very strikingly different from that of *B. variegata,* and supply an easy method of distinguishing. The petals of *B. purpurea* do not overlap (as they do in *B. variegata*), and they are not so stiff, but tend to be narrow, straplike and floppy. *B. variegata* has five stamens; *B. purpurea* has three, or rarely four.

Because of the confusion existing in California and Texas, where plants of *"B. purpurea"* are offered in the trade and widely planted, it should be noted here that all those we have checked have turned out to be of *B. variegata.* We do not know why *B. purpurea* does not grow in these areas, but all herbarium specimens we have seen and live plants grown from seed from these areas, and information from correspondence, show that even though the plants may be called *B. purpurea,* they turn out to be plants that flower during the winter months and have wide petals. Therefore, so far as we can determine, the common *Bauhinia* that is cultivated in southern California and southern Texas is *B. varieaata.*[5]

The "pink orchid tree" usually seen in Florida is *B. monandra,* a small ornamental tree from Burma. Sometimes it is called Jerusalem date or Butterfly Flower. It is deciduous through the winter months. The tree produces great quantities of big flowers at the branch tips from May to November and is seldom without blossoms through that period. When the flower first opens, the top petal (standard) is a great splash of red on a bright yellow background. The other four petals are white or very pale pink, liberally splattered with red dots. After twenty-four hours, the red, yellow and white all change to a bold pink color. The seed pod is thick, about six inches long, and pops open when the seeds are ripe. Synonyms for *B. monandra* are *B. kappleri* Sagot, *B. krugii* Urban, and *Caspareopsis monandra* Britt. and Rose. In New Orleans a specimen of *B. monandra* was killed by twenty-six degrees.

We find that it is almost impossible to tell *B. variegata, B. purpurea* and *B. monandra* apart by their leaves alone. Consequently, we submit the main characters by which we separate these three common species:

Bauhinia purpurea	Bauhinia variegata	Bauhinia monandra
1. Flowers in fall (Oct.-Dec.).	1. Flowers in winter and spring (Jan.-April).	1. Flowers in summer (April-Oct.).
2. Flowers while leaves are on the trees.	2. Flowers while leaves are falling or after they have fallen.	2. Flowers while leaves are on the tree.
3. Inflorescence many flowered, near ends of long whiplike branches.	3. Inflorescence few flowered, on short lateral branches.	3. Inflorescence few-flowered on short lateral erect branches.
4. Petals narrow, to ¾ inch wide.	4. Petals wider, to 1¼ inch wide.	4. Petals to one inch wide.
5. Petals oblanceolate.	5. Petals obovate.	5. Petals obovate.
6. Petals not overlapping.	6. Petals overlapping.	6. Petals not overlapping.
7. Calyx usually splitting into two sections.	7. Calyx split in one piece only.	7. Calyx split in one piece only.
8. Stamens three (rarely four).	8. Stamens five.	8. Stamen only one.
9. Hypanthium shorter than the calyx limb.	9. Hypanthium as long as or longer than the calyx limb.	9. Hypanthium as long as or longer than the calyx limb.

171. BAUHINIA PURPUREA (Fall-blooming orchid)

170. BAUHINIA MONANDRA
(Jerusalem thorn, Butterfly flower

The Hong Kong Bauhinia

Unquestionably the most spectacular and most exciting "orchid tree" of them all is the evergreen Hong Kong species, *B. blakeana* Dunn. It first flowered in Florida in 1953 from a layer obtained in Hong Kong and brought into the United States by the Sub-Tropical Experiment Station. Since then it has been propagated vegetatively by grafting and air layering so that it is commercially available now. The fragrant flowers are "orchidlike," five and a half to six inches across; the color is a rich reddish or rose purple, almost a crimson, and the color does not fade. Flowers are produced from October to March, each blossom lasting three to four days. For a more complete description of *B. blakeana,* see the *National Horticultural Magazine,* July 1954. G. A. C. Herklots, in the April 1948 issue of *Food and Flowers,* a bulletin issued by the Gardens Department of the Hong Kong government, wrote:

"Hong Kong possesses its own *Bauhinia* which is probably the most beautiful tree of this genus in the world. Its origin is unknown and as it never produces seed it is possibly a sterile hybrid. The tree was originally described by Mr. S. T. Dunn in the *Journal of Botany* for 1908, page 325. Accompanying the description were these comments:

" 'The trivial name of this species commemorates the kindly interest taken in the Hong Kong Botanical Gardens by Sir Henry and Lady Blake during the governorship of the former, which ended in

[5] Other species cultivated in protected areas in California besides *B. variegata* and its variety *candida,* are *B. candicans, B. tomentosa* (as *B. natalensis*), *B. galpinii, B. saigonensis, B. corymbosa, B. grandiflora* (?), *B. acuminata, B. carronii. B. variegata* is also grown in southern Texas, especially near Brownsville. *B. divaricata* (given as *B. mexicana* in Baileys' Manual) is apparently very hardy as it is cultivated in Austin, Texas, and takes temperatures of twenty-six degrees. *B. forficata* probably is quite hardy and may take cold weather.

1903. The tree is at present a very rare one in cultivation and is likely for some time to remain so, as it can only be propagated by cuttings. This is the more to be regretted because out of the numerous cultivated species of this charming family there is probably none that equals it either in the beauty or the profusion of its flowers. For more than four months the trees remain covered with their large, reddish-purple blooms which develop successively on the long racemes.

" 'The only trees known to exist at the present time are those in the Hong Kong Botanical Gardens, a few near the sanatorium of the Mission Etrangeres at Pokfulem, on the other side of the island, and a few more at the Roman Cathedral at Canton. It is indeed to the fathers of the above Mission that we owe the preservation of this *Bauhinia.* It was discovered by them near the ruins of a house on the seashore, and cuttings were planted in their garden; from the trees thus produced the Botanic Gardens were supplied. Specimens have been compared in the Kew and other herbaria, but without the discovery of any similar plant from elsewhere. Its native country must remain for the present obscure.' "

Shrubs and Small-Leaved Trees

Two summer-blooming shrubs of the genus *Bauhinia* are cultivated in South Florida. One is the white-flowered Indian plant, *B. acuminata,* and the South African scandent shrub, *B. galpinii,* with its spectacular brick-red flowers suggesting oversize nasturtiums. Both bloom prolifically from May to October and are bare of leaves or nearly so in winter. *B. galpinii* sustains several degrees of frost, is much cultivated in southern California, and will climb trees or lend itself to espaliering. Plants at Homestead and Miami often set a few seed pods from late fall flowers and the seeds are ready by February; elsewhere through Florida the plants rarely set seed. *B. galpinii* occasionally looks ratty if the leaf-cutting

173. BAUHINIA DIVARICATA (Pata de Vaca)

172. BAUHINIA FASSOGLENSIS

wasps go to work on the leaves; they seem to have a special preference for this species of *Bauhinia*. *B. acuminata* sets quantities of seed, and it flowers profusely all summer. It sometimes needs a nutritional spray to keep the foliage healthy, and, if taken care of, it is a very ornamental shrub.

Three Queensland, Australia, species are in cultivation in Florida but, so far as we know, they have not flowered here. They are *B. hookeri, B. cunninghamii* and *B. carronii*. All three are very similar in appearance, with leaves that are small and cut completely to the base to form two leaflets. *B. carronii* has gray-green, drooping foliage with growth habit suggestive of the Chinese *Ginkgo*. Eventually twenty feet, the tree has scarlet flowers and will stand twelve degrees of frost. Sometimes this tree is called Queensland Ebony. *B. hookeri* reaches forty feet, with clustered white flowers edged crimson. *B. cunninghamii* grows to fifteen feet and has rosy-red flowers massed along the branches when bare of leaves; var. *rosea* is a southern Queensland dwarf form with white flowers faintly tinged rose.

The Yellow Mix-Up

Now begins an exposition of one of several most confusing problems attendant upon the genus *Bauhinia*. *B. tomentosa* is native to India, southern China, Ceylon, and tropical Africa and has become naturalized in Jamaica, Puerto Rico, and other West Indian islands. In Hawaii it is called St. Thomas tree. Because of its wide range, it apparently exists in several different forms and there is great confusion in botanical gardens, herbaria, floras, nursery catalogues, etc., in naming this species. The typical form seems to be that which produces flowers that are bright yellow in color. This type is usually a small tree or large shrub to twelve feet often trimmed low as a hedge; the flowers may be produced only in the fall on some plants, others flower off and on

through the summer and fall. Quite unlike the "orchid" flowers of other *Bauhinia* under discussion, the petals of *B. tomentosa* are half-wrapped to form a tube about two inches long. This rarely opens more than an inch wide at the mouth. Down in the throat is frequently a pencil-size jet-black or chocolate dot, but this may be red or missing entirely.

Also cultivated in Florida is a form of this tree with light yellow, almost whitish flowers, that is being called *B. picta*. The true *B. picta*, however, is an entirely different species. It is native to Colombia, its leaves are entire; it has terminal racemes with white petals spotted with red. So far as we know, it has never been brought into cultivation.

The so-called *B. picta* grown and sold in South Florida was brought into this country by the U. S. Department of Agriculture (P.I. 141550) in 1941, and by the Sub-Tropical Experiment Station, (SES 2029) in 1940, both as seeds from the Atkins Garden in Cuba. The Director of that Garden reported that this plant came to them from the Botanic Garden in Saigon, Indo-China, in 1935, as a seed. We have written to this Garden but have never received a reply. Apparently the name *B. picta* was applied by the Saigon Botanical Garden to the species in question. But we think it is time that the name "picta" be dropped from this form of *B. tomentosa*.

Another form of *B. tomentosa,* this time not differing in color of the flower, but in the habit of growth and the size of the leaves, has been masquerading under the name of *B. natalensis* (or sometimes spelled *B. "taitensis"*). We have grown this from seed from California, South Africa, and Kenya, East Africa, and all the plants have proved to be *B. tomentosa*. We suspect that this form with small leaves and peculiar habit of branching might be the South African form of *B. tomentosa*. The true *B. natalensis* Oliver does not seem to be in cultivation. Herbarium specimens and de-

175. BAUHINIA MOLLICELLA

174. BAUHINIA GLAUCA

scriptions in the literature refer to the true *B. natalensis* as a small shrub, with the leaf *completely* divided to the base to form two distinct leaflets, petals spreading, white with some of them reddish in color along the veins, the pods small and flat. Certainly the true *B. natalensis* is not what we are cultivating in Florida. In our opinion all of this material should be referred to variations of *B. tomentosa*.

One of the interesting facts about all these forms of *B. tomentosa* is that the flowers fade from the various depths of yellow to dull shades of purple and brown and red.

Orchid Trees With Thorns

The thorny species of *Bauhinia*—and there are a good many—are in extreme confusion. *B. mollicella, B. pauletia* and *B. aculeata* present no problem, but *B. forficata, B. candicans, B. corniculata,* and *B. grandiflora* need some clarification. We are convinced that the plants in cultivation are all *B. forficata* and that *B. candicans* is the same and should be put under synonymy or else we do not have it in cultivation. We have not been able to satisfy ourselves yet on *B. corniculata*[6] or *B. grandiflora,* as specimens have not been available, hence we cannot determine whether they are valid species. The descriptions in the literature are not helpful.

The following is a detailed description of *B. forficata* which, in our opinion, fits many of the large-flowering, spiny *Bauhinia*:

Bauhinia forficata Link, Enum. Hort. Berol. 1:404. 1891

(*B. aculeata* Vell., *B. candicans* Benth. or Hort.?, *B. corniculata* Benth or Hort.?, *B. furfuracea* Hort., *B. grandiflora* Juss. or Hort.?, *B. longiflora* D. Diev.)

Small thorny tree or large shrub, to 15-20 feet, with upright or spreading branches, the latter often zig-zag. Young green branches only slightly hairy or clothed with fuzzy hairs. Leaves petioled to 1 in.; blades variable in size and shape to 4 in. long and 3½ in. wide, longer than broad, cleft ½, the lobes relatively long and narrow and pointing upward and acute or obtuse, base round or cordate, sinus usually rounded, dark green; blades somewhat stiff and thickened, pale glaucous and usually pubescent below, especially on the veins, or glabrous, veins 9-11 with characteristic reticulate veins below. Stipules to ¼ in., awl-like. Thorns 2 at each node, sharp, strong, usually one pointing downward or both pointing downward, dark tipped, to ¼ in. long; sometimes only one thorn developed or individual trees may be entirely thornless.

Inflorescence opposite leaves, of 2-4 flowers, but usually in pairs, produced on new branches in spring, peduncle practically absent. Flowers large and showy, white, cup-like, 3-5 in. in diameter, slightly fragrant, pedicelled to ¼ in.; buds long and narrow to 2¾ in., pointed, hairy. Calyx splitting down one side and falling back, boat shaped, pale whitish green; petals 5, white, usually fading to a cream color, long and narrow, 2½ to 4 in. long, ¼ to ½ in. wide, with a very prominent midrib, spreading out, all more or less alike in size and shape, crinkly margin, oblanceolate, irregularly cut or indented, very short clawed. Stamens 10, filaments white, long and prominent, curved to one

---

[6] *B. corniculata* of California appears to be identical to what we have been calling *B. forficata. B. candicans, B. corniculata* and *B. grandiflora* we think, at least as these plants exist in cultivation, are *B. forficata*. These may be good species in the wild, but the plants so called in cultivation seem to all be *B. forficata*. Examination of herbarium specimens and notes taken from various floras shows that in *B. corniculata* the stamens and styles are red in color, the petals greenish-white. The inflorescence is a raceme to 8 inches long, usually with thorns as well as leaves on the rachis. The flower buds become 1½ inches long; the flowers are 2½-3 inches long and 3 inches in diameter; petals 1 inch across. The leaves have only a very shallow cleft, less than one third the distance.

176. BAUHINIA FORFICATA

177. BAUHINIA TRIANDRA

side of flower, of different length, white hairy at base, attached by a short membrane to each other at base, anthers ¾ in. long. Hypanthium to ¾ in., cylindric, white hairy, ovary stipate, style long and curved, stigma two parted. Pods to 6-8 in. long and ¾ in. wide, flat, brown, woody, stalked, narrow at base and widest above the middle, peaked; seeds to ⅜ in., brown.

B. forficata is an unusual species—the flowers are large and showy, opening at night and fading by the end of the next day. The thorns are quite prominent, and sharp. It is deciduous in winter, and flowers appear in April and May and continue off and on throughout the summer to September. It is native to Peru, Brazil, Argentina, Paraguay, and Uruguay. It was cultivated in England as early as 1837, and has been in this country for many years. C. T. Simpson mentions (as B. furfuracea) growing it in 1912 in Miami. Several introductions and distributions have been made by the U. S. Department of Agriculture.

It is sometimes sold under the name of B. candicans (not to be confused with B. variegata var. candida) or as B. grandiflora, although this latter name has been used for a variety of B. purpurea. There are slight variations in the shape of the leaf, depth of its cleft, amount of pubescence, size of the flowers, and this probably has given rise to the numerous synonyms. In California, it is called B. corniculata.

It is said to be one of the hardiest of the Bauhinia species and probably can be grown in North Florida as well as in southern Georgia.

178. BAUHINIA VARIEGATA (Florida orchid, Mountain ebony)

180. BAUHINIA DIPHYLLA

179. BAUHINIA BLAKEANA (Hong-Kong orchid)

Key to the Cultivated Species of Bauhinia

A. Vines climbing with the aid of tendrils.
 B. Leaves cleft to the base, thus forming two separate leaflets.
  C. Petals white, stamens sometimes red............................ 1. *B. binata*
  C. Petals pink, some of them with red stripes...................... 7. *B. saigonensis*
 B. Leaves not cleft to the base, merely two-lobed.
  C. Petals bright yellow.. 4. *B. fassoglensis*
  C. Petals not bright yellow.
   D. Leaves glabrous; stamens 10; petals white, one concave and spotted with red... 3. *B. cumanensis*
   D. Leaves pubescent; stamens less than 10.
    E. Stamens 7 or 8; petals yellowish-green.................. 6. *B. macrostachys*
    E. Stamens 3; petals white to cream or pinkish.
     F. Leaves to one foot long and wide; pubescence white or rust colored.. 8. *B. vahlii*
     F. Leaves smaller; pubescence red silky.
      G. Leaves to one inch long and wide, cleft to below the middle... 2. *B. corymbosa*
      G. Leaves to 3½ inches long and wide, cleft to only one third.. 5. *B. hupehana*
A. Shrubs or trees, or if climbing, tendrils absent.
 B. Stems with spines at base of leaves but above the stipules.
  C. Flowers yellow-green, not showy.
   D. Petals to 3 inches long, hair-like, coiled back.............. 12. *B. pauletia*
   D. Petals to ⅜ inch long, ¼ inch broad, not hair-like nor coiled back.. 26. *B. polycarpa*
  C. Flowers white and showy.
   D. Flowers 2 to 2½ inches in diameter......................... 9. *B. aculeata*
   D. Flowers 3 to 5 inches in diameter.
    E. Leaves conspicuously soft velvety pubescent above and below; inflorescence a short corymb of 4 or more flowers; petals to 2½ inches long................................. 11. *B. mollicella*
    E. Leaves glabrous or if pubescent mostly on veins below; inflorescence of 2 or 3 flowers; petals 3 inches or more long..... 10. *B. forficata*
 B. Stems without spines.
  C. Leaves cleft to the base, thus forming two separate leaflets.
   D. Petals nearly all equal in size and shape; inflorescence of more than 2 or 3 flowers.
    E. Vine-like shrub; petals obovate, one inch long, white; stamens and style usually red; inflorescence a dense axillary corymb.. 1. *B. binata*
    E. Tree; petals ovate, white with crimson markings; stamens and style white; inflorescence a short terminal raceme......... 22. *B. hookeri*
   D. Petals of different size, 2 longer, 2 shorter, and one as long as the calyx lobes; inflorescence of 2 or 3 flowers opposite the leaves.
    E. Calyx lobes ⅝ inch long; calyx tube short and broad; petals ovate... 21. *B. cunninghamii*
    E. Calyx lobes ⅜ inch long; calyx tube long and narrow; petals obovate.. 20. *B. carronii*
  C. Leaves not cleft to the base, merely two-lobed or entire.
   D. Leaves entire, obtuse or with a small notch at the apex: petals pale cream or yellow, 3 with irregular dark spots............ 29. *B. retusa*
   D. Leaves cleft from ¼ to ¾, producing two lobes.
    E. Petals brick-red in color; sprawling shrub sometimes climbing.. 16. *B. galpinii*
    E. Petals not brick-red; erect shrubs or trees.

217

F. Petals yellow or cream-colored, with a dark spot at base of one petal inside; flowers bell-shaped, pendant, to 2½ inches long... 18. *B. tomentosa*

F. Petals and flowers not as described above.

  G. Petals narrow, linear or hair-like, to 3 or 4 inches long; stamens 10, as long or longer than the petals.

    H. Calyx and calyx tube conspicuously brown or reddish brown tomentose .... 24. *B. megalandra*

    H. Calyx tube not brown tomentose .... 12. *B. pauletia*

  G. Flowers not as described above.

    H. Flowers relatively small, less than 2 inches in diameter.

      I. Fertile stamen only one, long protruding; petals white, usually turning to pale or deep pink with age .... 14. *B. divaricata*

      I. Fertile stamens 10.

        J. Leaves very small, less than ½ inch long, cleft ¾; branches short, produced in a flat plane .... 30. *B. rufescens*

        J. Leaves larger, cleft ¼ to ½; branches not in a flat plane.

          K. Leaves conspicuously reticulate below; inflorescence a hanging raceme; petals not spreading, to ¾ inch long .... 23. *B. malabarica*

          K. Leaves relatively thin; inflorescence erect.

            L. Flowers to ¾ inch in diameter, white; petals all alike and spreading, short clawed .. .. 15. *B. faberi*

            L. Flowers ½ inch or less in diameter, not showy; petals not clawed.

              M. Petals oval, erect, not spreading, forming a cup-like flower; petiole conspicuously grooved .... 26. *B. polycarpa*

              M. Petals linear, recurved and recoiled; petiole not grooved ...... 28. *B. racemosa*

    H. Flowers large and showy, 2 to 6 inches in diameter.

      I. Fertile stamen one; plants flowering during the summer months .... 25. *B. monandra*

      I. Fertile stamens more than one.

        J. Fertile stamens 3 (or 4); plants flowering in the fall months .... 27. *B. purpurea*

        J. Fertile stamens more than 3.

          K. Fertile stamens 5 (or 6); trees.

            L. Flowers purple or reddish-purple.

              M. Flowers to 4 inches in diameter, produced in winter and spring, in short clusters of 3 to 7; petals overlapping .... 31. *B. variegata*

              M. Flowers to 5½ and 6 inches in diameter, produced from October to March in elongating racemes; petals not overlapping .... 19. *B. blakeana*

            L. Flowers white .... 32. *B. variegata* var. *candida*

          K. Fertile stamens 10 (rarely 8); shrubs flowering in the summer .... 13. *B. acuminata*

Below are short descriptions of most of the *Bauhinia* species in cultivation. Those best adapted to Peninsular Florida and considered the most attractive species are marked with an asterisk.

Vines

*1. *B. binata* Blanco (*B. blancoi* Baker, *B. pinnata* Walp.). Native to southeastern Asia. Introduced by Dr. David Fairchild in 1940 from Nanipo Island, Moluccas, and distributed by the USDA (P. I. 139345). Vinelike shrub, resembling *B. galpinii* but the new growth possesses coiled tendrils. Leaves completely divided into two separate small, oval leaflets. Flowers white, starlike, to 2 inches across, produced in dense axillary and terminal corymbs from April to June. Stamens 10, white, in age usually becoming red.

2. *B. corymbosa* Roxb. (*B. scandens* Burm.) "Phanera." Native to South China. Said to be one of the most attractive species of *Bauhinia* vines; it has been grown in many countries including Hawaii and has been tried in southern California but in South Florida it has not been very successful. Leaves small, cleft to below the middle. Flowers to 1 inch across, pale pinkish or rose colored, or white with pink venation, the petals spreading and nearly all alike, produced in elongating racemes throughout the summer months. Stamens 3.

*3. *B. cumanensis* HBK (*B. heterophylla* Kunth.). "Turtle vine.' Native to western Cuba, Trinidad, and northern South America. Introduced into Florida from Cuba by C. T. Simpson nearly 50 years ago. In 1940 it was distributed by the USDA (P. I. 110893). Older stems become woody, flat and twisted and with turtle-shaped swellings. Leaves of two types, those cleft to the middle and those on young shoots that are cut nearly to the base. Flowers white, fragrant, to 1½ inches across, produced in short axillary and terminal elongating racemes from June to October. Stamens 10. Rarely fruits in Florida.

4. *B. fassoglensis* Kotschy ex. Schweinf. Native from Central Sudan to Transvaal, South Africa. Introduced by the USDA (P. I. 133442 and 113837) in the late 1930's. The few specimens in South Florida have grown well and they flower profusely but fail to set fruit. It is a scandent shrub, the leaves nearly round in outline and notched only a short distance. Flowers are bright yellow, to 3 inches across, produced in long racemes off and on throughout the year. Stamens only 2.

5. *B. hupehana* Carib. Native to Central China. Introduced in 1926 and again in 1936 (P. I. 114718). In both cases the USDA distributed plants for trial in Florida. It has been grown as far north as Gainesville, Fla., under *Bauhinia*

fassoglensis | *cumanensis*

vahlii | *saigonensis*

All photos of J. C. Noonan

slat shade. Leaves cleft less than 1/3. Flowers 1½ inches across, fragrant, white, usually tinged with pink, produced in elongating corymblike racemes from March to June. Stamens 3.

6. *B. macrostachys* Wall. (*B. scandens* Roxb..). Native to India and cultivated in the Orient and at the Atkins Botanical Garden in Cuba. Recently introduced to Florida by the Sub-Tropical Experiment Station. Leaves cleft ¼. Flowers yellowish-green, to 1½ inches across, appearing in late summer and fall. Stamens 7 or 8.

*7. *B. saigonensis* Pieere ex Gagnepain. "Saigon Bauhinia." This species was discovered in 1912 in the State of Cochin Chine, French Indo-China, was introduced to the United States by the USDA in 1937 (P. I. 129188) and distributed for trial in 1939 and 1940. It has been grown successfully in northern Florida and also in southern California. A delicate but hardy attractive vine with leaves completely divided into two leaflets. Flowers pink-lavender with red veins, to 1½ inches across, produced in elongating racemes from April to November. Stamens 3.

8. *B. vahlii* Wight and Arnott (not *B. racemosa* Vahl.). "Malu or Maloo creeper." Native to northern India. It has been in Florida for many years and was offered by the Royal Palm Nursery at Oneco, Florida, before 1900. A recent introduction that accounts for the plants in South Florida at the present time was made by the USDA in 1932 (P. I. 98803). This is one of the most spectacular of the Bauhinia species—a gigantic climber to 100 feet, hardly suitable for the average garden, but sometimes found in special collections. The trunk may become 4 inches in diameter and is often deeply fluted. The leaves are very large, to 12 inches long and wide, cleft ¼. The flowers are cream-colored, 2 to 2½ inches across, produced in elongating terminal corymblike racemes from April to October. Stamens 3.

Species with Thorns—Shrubs or Small Trees

9. *B. aculeata* L. (*B. albiflora* Britt. and Rose, *B. emarginata* Mill., *B. ungula* Jacq.). Native to the Lesser Antilles and northern South America. Introduced in 1932 by Dr. Fairchild from seeds collected on Cannouan Island near Trinidad (P. I. 97864). Shrub to 12 feet with conspicuous, sharp, curved thorns, 2 at a node. Leaves cleft ¼. Flowers resembling *B. acuminata,* white, 2½ inches across, produced in clusters of 1 to 3 opposite a leaf and appearing in May and June. Stamens 10.

10. *B. forficata* Link

*11. *B. mollicella* Blake. Native to Venezuela and Colombia. Introduced by the USDA in 1935 (P. I. 110895) and distributed for trial in Florida in 1941. The best of the white-flowering thorny species and much preferred to *B. forficata.* Large spreading shrub or tree to 20 feet, thorns 2 at a node. Leaves soft velvety pubescent, cleft ¼. Flowers large and showy, 3 to 4 inches across, white fading to a cream color, produced 1 to 5 together, appearing from April to October. Stamens 10.

219

182. BAUHINIA RETUNDATA

181. BAUHINIA ACUMINATA

12. *B. pauletia* Persoon (*B. aculeata* Cav.). "Railway Fence Bauhinia." Native to Central America from western Mexico to Panama, also Venezuela and Trinidad and escaped in Puerto Rico. In certain countries it is often found growing along roadsides and railroad rights-of-way, hence the common name. Introduced by the USDA in 1941 (P. I. 141549) for trial in South Florida. Shrub or small tree to 16 feet. Spines stout and sharp, two at each node. Leaves notched ¼ or less. Flowers unusual, large but relatively inconspicuous because of the narrow, yellowish-green hairlike petals that are 3 inches long; flowers produced in a raceme from October to January. Stamens 5. Grown as an oddity.

Shrubs—Not Thorny

*13. *B. acuminata* L. (not *B. petioliata* as listed in USDA Circular No. 34, *Some Ornamental Shrubs for the Tropics, 1951*), "Dwarf white Bauhinia." Native to southeastern Asia and has been in cultivation in this country since before 1900. Shrub to 10 feet. Leaves cleft 1/3. Flowers showy, pure white, to 4 inches across, produced in elongating racemes from May to October. Stamens 10.

*14. *B. divaricata* L. (*B. aurita* Griseb., *B. mexicana* Vogel., *B. porrecta* SW., *B. ungulata* L.) "Pata de Vaca." Variable species native to the Greater Antilles and Central America from Mexico to Guatemala. Has been cultivated in Texas as far north as Austin and subjected to temperatures as low as 10°F. Introduced to Florida in 1951 as seed from Texas, Cuba, and Jamaica. Shrub or small tree to 16 feet. Leaves variable in size and shape, usually cleft about 1/3. Flowers unusual, white, usually turning pink with age, 1½ inches across, produced in short elongating racemes off and on throughout the year. Stamen only 1.

15. *B. faberi* Oliver (*B. godefroyi* Gag.). Native to Indo-China and first introduced in 1914 (P. I. 40708) and again in 1937 (P. I. 129190) by the USDA and distributed in 1939-40. Spreading shrub to 12 feet with graceful arching branches. Leaves cleft to the middle. Flowers white, small, to ¾ inch in diameter, produced on short axillary racemes from May to September. Stamens 10.

*16. *B. galpinii* N. E. Br. (*B. punctata* Bolle). "Red or Nasturtium Bauhinia." Native to South Africa; discovered in 1890, cultivated in England in 1895 and within a few years it had appeared in various countries throughout the world. First cultivated in Florida in 1903 near Jacksonville. Low, spreading shrub with long branches that if given support will climb without the aid of tendrils. Leaves cleft to less than ½. Flowers large and showy, brick red in color, 2½ inches across, petals more or less erect and little spreading. Stamens 3. Flowers appear from May to October on new growth as it elongates. The axillary inflorescences of 2 to 10 flowers each are produced at every third node.

17. *B. petersiana* Bolle. Native of tropical Africa and reported in cultivation in Trinidad and Calcutta. It is a climbing shrub with leaves cleft to the middle, the flowers large, white or pale yellow, the petals narrow and with colored markings. Several recent introductions have been made in Florida but to date none has flowered and therefore we are uncertain of the true identity of this species at the present time.

*18. *B. tomentosa* L. (not *B. natalensis* Oliver, not *B. picta* DC., not *B. taitensis* Hort.). "Yellow or Bell Bauhinia." Native to India, South China, Ceylon, and tropical South Africa and cultivated in many tropical countries. It was grown in Florida before 1900. Shrub or small tree to 15 feet, variable in growth habit. Flowers bell shaped, drooping, the petals overlapping, bright sulphur yellow or cream colored, fading to brownish red. Stamens 10.

Trees

*19. *B. blakeana* Dunn. "Hong Kong Bauhinia."

20. *B. carronii* F. Muell. "Queensland Ebony." Native to Queensland, Australia. Grown to a limited extent in southern California and recently introduced to South Florida where it has not flowered yet. Small tree to 20 feet with drooping branches. Leaves divided into 2 small leaflets. Flowers white, the petals spreading, edged with purple, produced 2 or 3 together. Stamens 10.

21. *B. cunninghamii* Benth. Native to Queensland, Australia, and introduced for trial in Florida by USDA (P. I. 194496 and 194497) in 1951, but no specimens have flowered yet. Tree to 15 feet with long arching branches. Leaves divided into 2 separate leaflets. Flowers rosy-red, or in variety *rosea* white or dull yellow with red markings, produced 2 or 3 together. Stamens 10.

22. *B. hookeri* F. Muell. Native to Queensland, Australia. Introduced to Florida a number of times but none of the plants have flowered yet. Large spreading tree to 40 feet. Leaves cleft to the base to form two separate leaflets. Flowers showy, 2 to 3 inches across, in large clusters, petals white bordered with crimson. Stamens 10.

23. *B. malabarica* Roxb. (not *B. reticulata* DC. of Africa). "Malabar Bauhinia." Native to India, Burma, Siam, and Java. It was listed by the Royal Palm Nursery in Oneco, Fla., as early as 1887, but the few trees in cultivation in Florida today are from introductions by the USDA in the late 1920's and early 1930's (P. I. 94181). Large spreading tree to 40 feet. Leaves cleft ¼. Flowers to ¾ inches long and wide, tubular, greenish white, in pendent racemes, appearing from late October through February. Stamens 10.

24. *B. megalandra* Griseb. Native to the Lesser Antilles from St. Kitts to Trinidad, and also in Venezuela. First introduced by Dr. Fairchild in 1932· (P. I. 99521). Small tree to 15 feet. Leaves cleft 1/3. Flowers similar to *B. pauletia*, long and narrow, to 5 inches long, the petals straplike, only ¼ to ⅜ inch wide, white, appearing in winter months, and produced singly opposite the leaves. Stamens 10.

221

184. BAUHINIA SCANDENS

183. BAUHINIA ANGUINA

*25. *B. monandra* Kurz. (*B. kappleri* Sagot, *B. krugii* Urban). Native to Burma and long in cultivation in tropical countries but it seems to have been in Florida only in the past 30 years. Small tree to 20 feet. Leaves cleft ⅓ to ½. Flowers large and showy, to 4 inches across, pink, produced in clusters of 5 to 9 in an axillary raceme from April to November. Stamen only 1.

26. *B. polycarpa* Wall. Native to Indo-China, Burma, and India. Introduced by the USDA in 1930 and distributed the following year (P. I. 86701). Small tree to 12 feet. Leaves cleft ⅓ to ½. Flowers small and inconspicuous, yellow-green, ¼ inch long, produced in short racemes, appearing from October to December. Stamens 10.

*27. *B. purpurea* L. (*B. alba* Hort., *B. grandiceps* Hort., *B. grandiflora* Hort., *B. rosea* Hort., *B. violacea* Hort., *B. triandra* Roxb.). Native to India, South China, Burma, Ceylon, Siam, and cultivated in many tropical countries. It arrived in Florida before 1900. Tree 20 to 40 feet tall. Leaves cleft ⅓ to ½. Flowers large and showy, 3 to 5 inches across, varying in color (see page 185), produced in elongating racemes near the ends of the branches, from October to December. Stamens 3.

28. *B. racemosa* L. Native to India, Ceylon, and Malaya. Introduced by the USDA in 1934 (P. I. 105728). Small tree to 20 feet. Leaves cleft ¼. Flowers white or pale yellow, and like *B. polycarpa,* small and inconspicuous, produced in short erect racemes from May to September. Stamens 10.

29. *B. retusa* Roxb. (*B. emarginata* Wall.). Native to northern India and introduced by the USDA in 1934 (P. I. 105870 and 105871). Tree to 20 feet. Leaves nearly entire, with only a small notch at the apex. Flowers 1 inch across, pale yellow or cream with dark purple-red spots, produced in a many-branched, elongating panicle from September to January. Stamens 3.

30. *B. rufescens* Lam. (*B. parviflora* Hochst., *B. rubescens* Bong.). Native to Central Africa and introduced into Florida by Menninger in the early 1940's. Small tree to 15 feet with odd manner of branching, producing flat-spreading branches in one plane. Leaves very small, less than ½ inch long, cleft ¾. Flowers white, ¾ inch long, not showy, produced in small racemes off and on throughout the year. Stamens 10. Pods black, and much coiled.

*31. *B. variegata* L. Native to southeastern Asia from South China to Dutch East Indies and in cultivation for many years in tropical countries; reported to be in the West Indies before 1700 and in Florida before 1900. It is also grown in California, Texas, and in protected areas in some of the Gulf States. Tree 20 to 40 feet tall. Leaves cleft ¼ to ⅓. Flowers large and showy, 4 to 5 inches across (see page 184 for color), produced in few-flowered, short, axillary inflorescences from February to March. Stamens 5.

*32. *B. variegata* L. var. *candida* Robx. (*B. alba* Buch.-Ham.). Similar to the preceding but the flowers lack all red, purple, and blue pigments and are pure white with the standard possessing greenish veins.

Other Species

B. anguina Roxb. "Snake Climber," is a vine with curious flattened stems and small white flowers; it is native to India and cultivated there. *B. championii* Benth. of Hong Kong is a vine recently introduced into Florida, but it has not flowered yet. *B. flammifera* Ridley, a vine native to the Malay Peninsula and cultivated there, has not as yet been grown successfully in Florida; it has yellow flowers that turn red with age. *B. diphylla* Hamilt. is a vine with tendrils and leaves divided to the base to form two distinct leaflets; the flowers are large, creamy white and with ten stamens; it is native to southeastern Asia and is cultivated in India. *B. glauca* Wall. of Burma, Malaya, and South China, is a woody climber with small white flowers in dense corymbs. Introduced by the USDA (P. I. 123844) in 1937. *B. involucellata* Kurz. is native to India and cultivated there; it is a climbing shrub without tendrils; has cleft leaves ½; petals pale rose, to 1½ inches long, the bracteoles on the pedicel enlarged to ⅓ inch to form a two leaved involucel to each flower. *B. phoenicea* Heyne is a scandent shrub native to and cultivated in India. *B. obtusata* Vog. of Brazil was introduced by the USDA in 1943 (P. I. 147597) and is represented at the U. S. Plant Introduction Garden in Coconut Grove; the flowers are similar to *B. megalandra.*

B. esculenta Berchill. "Tamani Berry" or "Gemsbok Bean," is a native of southwestern Africa. It is said to be a tree to 40 feet, but usually seen as a prostrate, trailing plant which can even be used as a ground cover. Seedlings grown at the Sub-Tropical Experiment station behave as vines and produce tendrils. The flowers are fragrant, a bright yellow color, with broad petals, produced on erect 4-inch stems in October and November. The roots are thick and of reddish color and, when dried, are boiled and eaten by the natives of Africa. The seeds are ½ inch in diameter and are an important source of food for the African Bushmen and also feed for cattle. The seeds are rich in protein and oils, the latter 42 per cent and of a pleasant taste. The oil is similar to cotton-seed oil and commercially is called "gemsbok oil."

185. CALLISTEMON SALIGNUS (Pink tip)

186. CALLISTEMON VIMINALIS (Weeping red bottlebrush)

The Bottlebrushes Like Wet Feet

Bottlebrush trees—the name commonly given to about fifteen species of *Callistemon* native to Australia—seem to offer Florida some much needed material for highway planting in low areas. Many of our roadside ditches are often called upon to carry heavy overflows, and flooding is detrimental to most trees. But the bottlebrushes are specially suited to low, damp, badly drained situations, some of them are fairly hardy, and they grow fast. Certainly these ornamentals from down under are worthy of extensive trial to determine which of them thrive under our growing conditions.

Two or three species of *Callistemon* have been grown by central and north Florida nurserymen for years, but the genus has been much neglected in the southern half of the state, and no planned effort has been made to get acquainted with other available species, some of which are more ornamental, grow better, and are generally more satisfactory than the common kind. Because of the need for an actual experience rating for the trees, the author has under cultivation in his garden in Stuart, Florida, the following species of *Callistemon* which represent practically every known member of this interesting family:

Callistemon phoenicius, Fiery Bottlebrush. This is a six-foot shrub from western Australia, with narrow, thick, veinless leaves and blossoms much like those of *C. citrinus* except that the growth is stiffer and exceedingly dense, the stamen brushes are bigger and a richer red, and the plant is a shrub rather than a tree. Lord[2] says: "This is probably the best and most brilliantly-flowered of all Australia's bottlebrushes. It does particularly well in

low, moist areas and relishes a clay soil. The narrowly-lanceolate leaves are two to four inches long. The seed pod buttons are often a half inch across.

C. salignus, Pink Tip. Willow Bottlebrush and White Bottlebrush are other accepted common names. It is a creamy-white-flowered tree from eastern Australia, with a paper bark, says de Beuzeville: *Australian Trees for Australian Planting,* and a very dense, shapely crown of small rather prickly-pointed, dark green leaves; "the young leaves and shoots form a foot-long terminal of beautiful pink tint, giving the plant a most ornamental appearance, and from which its popular name is derived." The tree flowers in Australia in late Spring (October-November), making a fine display of bloom, and the pink tips linger for some time after the flowers disappear. The creamy or pale yellow stamens (rarely light pink) are usually under a half inch in length. The tree prefers a moist situation, thriving in badly drained areas; it grows fast, gives good shade, stands some salt, likes clay soils, and is moderately frost resistant. It does well on dry land, if watered. Pink Tip is a good tree for highway planting under telephone wires, as it rarely exceeds 15 feet, though occasionally it may go to forty feet. The timber is one of the hardest of all Australian woods.

C. pinifolius viridis, Green-Flowering Bottlebrush. This amazing New South Wales tree looks like a pine (*Pinus* sp.) because it has rigid two to four-inch needlelike leaves, and its Kelly-green bottlebrush flowers, produced in spring when the plant is less than two feet high, could scarcely be called beautiful, but they are in striking contrast to the dark green foliage. I first saw this rare tree in one of Peter Riedel's parks in Santa Barbara, California, growing on a clay hillside. It also likes moist situations. George W. Althofer of the Nindethana Nursery,

---

[2]Ernest E. Lord, *Shrubs and Trees for Australian Gardens.*

188. CALLISTEMON CITRINUS (Lemon bottlebrush)

187. CALLISTEMON RUGULOSUS (Crimson bottlebrush)

Dripstone, New South Wales, writes: "An interesting thing I noticed about *C. pinifolius* along Duck Creek, Auburn, was that both the brilliant crimson and bottle-green forms grew there side by side. There was also a number of in-between colors. The progeny of the bottle-green plant, however, could not be depended on to give a hundred per cent green flowers. At least thirty per cent were red and a smaller number pale reds or yellowish."

C. speciosus, Showy Bottlebrush. Albany Bottlebrush is also an accepted common name. Ivo Hammet considers this West Australian species the finest of all the bottlebrushes, with *C. phoenicius* a runner-up. Certainly in Florida it has proved itself the most spectacular in bloom. It makes a handsome, bushy tree to twenty feet. The deep-red flower spikes to six inches long are tipped with gold, and, although spring is the accepted blooming time, it repeats frequently through the year. The narrow, two to four-inch lance-shaped leaves have a prominent midrib. Ernest E. Lord, in *Shrubs and Trees for Australian Gardens,* recommends that this tree be freely used in gardens and in highway planting. In this connection Mr. Lord sent a photograph with this comment: "The photo of the bottlebrush (*Callistemon* sp.) is taken from a few feet away but shows both flowers and leaves perfectly. The plant is in the shrubby stage at time of photographing, with flowers right to the ground. This is the general habit of most species of *Callistemon* with us for many years. Eventually some of them do become treelike with a single trunk, given a little pruning below. I call to mind a street in Hornsby, an outer suburb of Sydney, where I tried to snap a record of magnificent bottlebrushes, perfect standards twelve feet high, blood red with blossom, but light was poor and I did not get a good picture. The *Callistemon* picture I am sending you is *C. citrinus* (Syn. *C. lanceo-*

latus), indigenous to our eastern states, but it could almost as well illustrate the Western Australian *C. speciosus* (slightly shorter leaves and with more gold on anthers), or *C. phoenicius* (more shrubby, but brilliant in flower). It takes us all our time to distinguish the species if we get a bit out of practice."

Some confusion of names resulted several years ago in Florida when the U. S. Department of Agriculture introduced a tree labelled *Melaleuca genistifolia* which should have been labelled *Callistemon speciosus*. Peter Riedel of Santa Barbara, California's leading authority on introduced plants, helped to clarify this mix-up: "Your specimen is *Callistemon speciosus*. It could not be *Melaleuca* because the stamens are not united in five bundles. I enclose a small sample of *M. genistifolia* of which the flowers are white. The error is excusable because Nicholson's *Dictionary of Gardening* says *M. genistifolia* has red flowers and H. M. Hall groups it with the red-flowered ones. I received the seed of the first *M. genistifolia* grown here direct from Professor J. H. Maiden, so there is but slight chance that it is incorrect."

C. violacea, Violet Bottlebrush. This rare plant is described in the catalog of Nindethana Nursery, Dripstone, N. S. W. as "a tall, dense-growing shrub with violet flower spikes. It reaches twelve feet."

C. lilacinus, Lilac Bottlebrush. E. Cheel, curator of the National Herbarium, New South Wales, wrote: "*C. hortensis* was raised from seed obtained from Berlin under the name *C. amoenus,* a yellow-flowering species, probably only a form of *C. salignus*. From *C. hortensis* I have obtained *C. lilacinus* [Cheel spells it lilacina.] which was probably obtained as a result of hybridism. The first batch of seedlings raised from seed of *C. hortensis* was planted out and at least three color forms were produced, two-thirds garnet-colord spikes like the parent plant,

189. CALLISTEMON BRACHYANDRUS

190. CALLISTEMON RIGIDUS (Stiff bottlebrush)

and the other third creamy-white and lilac-colored species. It would seem that *C. hortensis,* misnamed *C. amoenus* by Berlin and Italian seed merchants, is also a result of hybridization." In Florida, this *C. lilacinus* has not yet bloomed for me, but D. J. McSwiney in Fort Lauderdale has bloomed the hybrid *C. lilacinus carmina,* an eight-foot shrub with carmine flower spikes and golden anthers.

C. linearis, Narrow-Leaf Bottle-brush. Harris writes in *Australian Plants for the Garden,* that this red-flowering form from sandy soils along the warmer east coast of Australia makes a fairly dense hedge ten to fif-teen feet high, if planted at four-foot intervals. The tree has long, stiff leaves and deep red brushes to six inches long in spring and summer. The four to five-inch narrow leaves are grooved on the upper surface.

C. citrinus, Lemon Bottlebrush. (Syn. *C. lanceolatus, C. acuminatus*). This commonest form of red-flowered bottlebrush tree has been planted through central and north Florida for years, to the neglect of many improved forms and better species. It makes a ten-foot bushy tree with faintly lemon-scented leaves. The flower heads are crimson, compact and upright. In Aus-tralia, this plant is often used for fairly dense hedges, planted at three to four-foot intervals. The most desirable im-proved form of this tree is known as *C. citrinus splendens,* a plant of garden origin raised many years ago at Kew from seed received as *C. laevis* from an Australian source that can no longer be traced. In moist climates like Eng-land and the San Francisco bay region of California, this tree is more spec-tacular in flower than *C. speciosus.* The young leaves are pink and silvery. The big bottlebrush flowers are shiny ver-milion, each stamen tipped with gold. The tree flowers with great freedom and makes a magnificent show. It is probably hardier than most of the bot-tlebrushes, and does not mind the cold of Feltham, Middlesex, England.

C. paludosus, Swamp Bottlebrush. This useful tree from the swampy lands of New South Wales grows from fif-teen to 30 feet high. It has narrow, sharp-pointed leaves and bears pale-yellow bottlebrush flowers in late spring or summer. It is a handsome plant for the bog garden.

C. viminalis, Weeping Red Bottle-brush. Much planted in both California and Florida, this makes a tree often to sixty feet, though normally much small-er and easily kept in bounds. It has a scaly bark, willowy branches, and four-inch light green leaves that are covered when young with bronzed hairs. These are found at the tips of all branches in spring and often are as ornamental as the long, red flower spikes that appear soon after the new foliage. In New South Wales, this tree, which grows naturally on river banks, is often alter-nated in hedges with the yellow-flow-ered *C. salignus* to provide a highly ornamental effect, as the trees bloom simultaneously.

C. rigidus, Stiff Bottlebrush. Though native to the rocky sandstone ledges near Sydney, New South Wales, this species is fast disappearing there. It is a fifteen-foot shrub with foliage to the ground, very stiff and slow-growing, with narrow, crowded, five-inch leaves, and bearing twice a year six-inch, dense, crimson bottlebrush flowers. It is much planted in sandy locations near the coast, and endures hard, dry con-ditions.

C. rugulosus, Crimson Bottlebrush. (Syn. *C. coccineus.*) This shrub of ten to fifteen feet from New South Wales is particularly happy in fresh water swamps, or in constantly wet sandy soil on the coast. It has rigid, rather narrow two-inch leaves, and bears large scarlet flower spikes in late summer or autumn. The spikes are short, but are described by Harris as "very handsome."

191. CORDIA BOISSIERI (Texas wild olive)

192. CORDIA ALLIODORA (Onion Cordia)

193. CORDIA SUPERBA

194. CORDIA GERASCANTHUS

The Geiger Tree and Its Relatives in Florida

Heliotrope and Forget-me-not are outstanding respresentatives of the Borage Family (BORAGINACEAE) in the Temperate Zone, but these are a far cry from the chief member of their family in the tropics—the genus *Cordia*. Practically all of the 280 *Cordia* species are trees, but only two of them are in what might be called common cultivation, one in South Florida, the other in Texas, which are the only places they are found in this country. Some botanists break down *Cordia* into several genera.

Because many *Cordia* trees are spectacular in bloom, the following notes on thirteen species under cultivation at Stuart, Florida, may be of interest:

Cordia sebestena. Commonly called "Geiger tree" in memory of an early pioneer in the Florida Keys, is the only showy-flowered Florida native tree that blossoms all the year 'round. Because of this habit, its evergreen foliage, and its rounded, moderate habit of growth, it is a favorite dooryard ornamental in the south half of the State where frost does not cut it down.

This is by all odds the best known of the *Cordia* trees and shrubs because it grows abundantly in the Keys, as well as throughout the West Indies, and for half a century has been cultivated as an ornamental. Its burnt-orange or vermilion, crepy, tubular flowers in clusters are from 1 to 2 inches long, usually an inch or more across, with six lobes. The bloom is followed by a white, apple-fragrant fruit one inch in diameter in which is imbedded one pear-shaped seed one-half inch or less in diameter. These sprout readily after being dried, but the trees are slow-growing and seedlings take three years to reach blooming size. Propagation by cuttings is not unusual.

Leaves of the Geiger tree are a beautiful dark green, but to the touch extremely rough, almost like sandpaper, and they vary a good deal in size, even on the same tree, from 4 to 9 inches long.

The Geiger tree never exceeds 25 feet in height, so lends itself to planting in average gardens. It blossoms both winter and summer and several times in between, maintaining no set schedule but depending perhaps more on the available moisture. The flowers are in loose clusters of 8 to 12, beyond the dark green foliage which makes a striking background for the brilliant color of the bloom.

Cordia dodecandra. A beautiful, tall tree of southern Mexico, sometimes to 100 feet, which I introduced from seed sent me by Thomas MacDougall from Tehauntepec. Record & Hess call this the most important species of the Boraginaceae in Guatemala, British Honduras, Yucatan and southern Mexico. It has six-inch, very rough, gray-green leaves, and the bright orange flowers resemble those of *C. sebestena* except they are much larger (often two inches across) and individually more spectacular, with twelve to seventeen petal lobes instead of five. My ten-foot tree blooms off and on all year, but so far is less prolific and showy in flower than *C. sebestena*. The edible acid fruits have not yet been produced.

Cordia alliodora. An evergreen tree, 25 to 40 feet or more with round crown and thick trunk, is called "onion Cordia" because the crushed leaves have an odor suggestive of garlic. It is the most widely distributed species, ranging from the West Indies and southern Mexico into the tropics as far as Peru. It bears small, white flowers in large clusters. Standley says: "it is exceptionally showy and conspicuous in flower because of the great abundance of white blossoms. These remain upon the tree for a long time (almost unshriveled), finally turn-

196. CORDIA SUBCORDATA

195. CORDIA SEBESTENA (Geiger tree)

ing brown and making the tree quite as conspicuous as when the corollas were pure white." The brown flowers finally serve as parachutes to the tiny falling fruits, the whole resembling a dried flower. In Trinidad the tree rises to 90 feet, often has girth to 10 feet, and is in demand for its tough but easily worked timber. This tree is also called *Cerdana alliodora*.

Cordia holsti. A rather crooked East African timber tree, which covered with its big heart-shaped, dull green leaves looks like a Catalpa. Jex-Blake calls it "very handsome" when covered with its very delicate, lacelike flowers, "but will only make a fine tree with heavy rainfall." In Florida, I found that it dropped its leaves repeatedly during our dry spells and was anything but an attractive ornamental most of the year and I gave up trying to grow it.

Cordia dentata. A small evergreen Mexican tree with rough leaves, bearing twice a year 10-inch clusters of light yellow, cup-shaped flowers, each one-half inch across. The flowers are pretty just for a day; they keep coming so the tree is attractive for several days in the blooming period, but disappointing the rest of the year. The half-inch yellow, jellylike fruits are sticky.

Cordia obliqua. A handsome shade tree from Cochin China with vigorous foliage and a good habit of growth that recommends it as an avenue tree. The spikes of white flowers are not showy. This species is hardier than most and will survive temperatures below freezing. It seeds prolifically in Florida.

Cordia nitida. The Puerto Ricans call this species *Cereza* (cherry) because of its cherrylike red fruits that are exceedingly attractive to birds, does not look like a *Cordia* at all. It has very glossy, dark green five-inch leaves, and sometimes grows to 70 feet though usually it is much smaller, even shrubby. Its many-flowered clusters of tiny, yellowish-white flowers are not

attractive, but the bright red fruits are pretty. Dr. Britton wrote of a tree at Coamo Springs; "It was loaded with fruit when we arrived. This was nearly all devoured by the birds that came to it morning and evening. The tree then bloomed profusely, was covered with small white flowers and set another crop of fruit before we came away." (Interval of 3 months). My "glossy Cordia", as it is sometimes called, is growing in a poultry run and it is the preferred roosting and feeding spot.

Cordia leucosebestena. Descriptions published by Grisebach a century ago in *Cat. Pl.Cub.*p.208, is a native of Cuba. He said the flowers were supposed to be white but he had never seen them. I spent ten years growing this tree in Florida and finally dug it out. Its dirty-white, crepy flowers, in size and shape like *C. sebestena,* are borne singly in Spring here and there over the tree, but they never look fresh even on first opening and they fall off at the slightest touch. The bushy, small-leaved tree with gray-green persistent foliage is not worth the space it takes. It never set fruit in Florida.

Cordia superba var. *elliptica*. This introduction from Kenya is one of great promise. It is a small tree with leathery, oblong-elliptic, dark green leaves to six inches long, about as big as a man's hand, densely stuck on the branches. Terminal clusters of 2-inch, showy white flowers make this an attractive and novel garden subject for Florida. It is rated by Chittenden as a better tree than *C. sebestena*.

Cordia lutea. Introduced from Ecuador twenty years ago by the USDA. It is an ornamental, much branched though sometimes straggling shrub, bearing clusters of bright yellow, trumpet-shaped ¾-inch flowers over a long summer. These are followed by small white fruits that are said to be edible.

Cordia boissieri. In its native Texas

is called the "wild olive", perhaps because its yellowish fruits are olive-shaped. Spanish-speaking folk on the border call it Anacahuita. It is a small evergreen tree to 20 feet bearing clusters of bright, pretty white 1½-inch crepy flowers, much like those of *C. sebestena*. It is more precocious than most *Cordia*, blooming when less than one foot high and it is hardy enough to take considerable cold without damage. It is propagated by seeds, though often with some difficulty. One Texas nurseryman sent me a quart of seeds from under his tree with a note: "Not much use to send these, as we cannot germinate them." However, I did sprout and grow scores of them.

Cordia angiocarpa. A Cuban tree with four-inch, gray-green, stiff, persistent leaves, very slow growing. Its flowers are burnt-orange color, rather like *C. dodecandra* but smaller. It bloomed first in 1954 and the initial display was scarcely a fair indication of its possibilities.

Cordia abyssinica. Eggeling: *Indigenous Trees of Uganda* says this shrub or tree to 30 feet has "very decorative" flowers, white, massed in compact panicles, appearing as if made of tissue paper. C. E. Duff's calendar for March in Northern Rhodesia calls this "a tree on anthills near Ndola, with great masses of white flowers which show up at long distances." I have succeeded in establishing this tree only this year, so its possibilities in Florida are unknown.

197. CORDIA DODECANDRA

199. DATURA ARBOREA (Angel's trumpet)

198. DATURA INOXIA

Datura Species in Florida Gardens

Florida homeowners cultivate half a dozen kinds of *Datura*, loosely called angel trumpets, mostly for their exceptionally large white, red, orange, yellow, or purple flowers, yet two anomalies crop up:

(1) Nobody ever picks *Datura* flowers for a bouquet. They may be the largest and most spectacular blossoms in the garden, but they stay on the plant and never get into the house.

(2) The *Datura* plants themselves are so varied, and the reference book descriptions of them are so mixed up and full of errors, that it is a rare gardener indeed who knows which *Datura* grows in his yard.

The flowers are avoided in bouquets not only because they are awkward, usually drooping instead of erect, and very short lived when removed from the plant, but because some kinds have flowers as well as foliage bearing offensive or narcotic odors, and this has made all of them outcasts. Actually a few kinds have flowers with a delightful fragrance, but these cannot live down the bad name of their relatives.

The confusion in nomenclature goes back several hundred years. No taxonomist has attempted a complete, systematic overhaul of the genus, with the result that the contradictory descriptions of the various species are overwhelming to the layman. Fortunately for the nonbotanist, partial examinations of the principal species in cultivation have been made recently by three scientists, Safford (1), Blakeslee (2), and DeWolf (3). By piecing these analyses together it is possible, with the aid of a few other reference works and some photographs, to explain in nontechnical language the essential distinctions between cultivated species and at last give correct names to some of the plants in Florida gardens.

Safford made the most comprehensive survey of the genus, defining 24 species, but complaining of the "great confusion in botanical literature in connection with the specific identity . . . of some of the most common species." Blakeslee held that "more studies are needed to clarify the taxonomy of the genus," and

DeWolf struggled with the "discrepancies and inaccuracies in the nomenclature."

The confusion these scholars speak of goes back to Linnaeus. His original description of *D. metel* (1753) was based on an Indian plant with glabrous leaves, the Asiatic "metel-nut" which had been used as a narcotic by the Arabs, Persians, and Hindus long before the discovery of America. It was described by Avicenna in the Eleventh Century. In the second edition of *Species Plantarum* (1762) Linnaeus seems to have overlooked the fact that he had originally described the glabrous Indian plant; now he inserted the word "pubescent," which is not true of the species he was describing, and the trouble began. Dunal in DeCandolle's *Prodromus* (1852) made matters worse by transferring the name *D. metel* from Asia to an American plant described by Miller (1768) under the name of *D. inoxia*. Several later botanists followed this lead, including C. B. Clarke in J. D. Hooker's *Flora of British India* who applied the name *D. metel* to the introduced American species of "downy thorn apple".

In the two principal modern reference works on general horticulture, Bailey (4) and Chittenden (5), these original confusions multiply. Bailey attributes *D. metel* to Linnaeus, then goes on to say that it has a 10-lobed corolla. This is true of the Mexican plant (*D. inoxia*) but not of the Indian (5 lobes). W. J. Bean in Chittenden says *D. metel* has flowers 10 inches long; this is not true for either the Indian plant or the Mexican. The flowers actually are 6-inches, rarely 7 inches long. Bailey picks up the Linnaean error of the second edition and calls *D. metel* pubescent; Bean says it is hairy. Neither of these authors describes the plant Linnaeus had in mind in his original text. Several varieties of the Indian *D. metel* are in common cultivation in Florida, hence the descriptions by Bailey and Bean do not apply. Bailey describes *D. fastuosa* L. as glabrous; Bean says it is "downy or glabrous"— (author plays safe!). Actually, *D. fastuosa* is only a purple-flowered

201. DATURA STRAMONIUM (Jimson weed)

200. DATURA STRAMONIUM (Purple form)

form of *D. metel,* so both authors contradict themselves.

This confusion goes on and on. Bean recognizes *D. cornigera* Hook., as a tree form to 10 feet; Bailey consigns it to the shrubs and says it is 3-4 feet. Whether this plant with its very fragrant white flowers grows in Florida, is uncertain.

Bailey and Bean both omit from the genus *Datura* any reference to *D. candida* (Pers.) Saff. the type for all the tree forms and certainly the commonest of them in cultivation. This may be partly because some early authors tried to put the South American tree forms into a new genus, *Brugmansia,* but the distinctions they sought to establish for this genus do not hold true, and *Brugmansia* now is properly regarded merely as the tree section of *Datura.* Even so, both reference books describe *"Datura arborea"* and other tree forms, so avoiding the principal species makes them inconsistent.

So much for the disordered background of the genus, though the ramifications continue to appear as the species under cultivation in Florida are examined.

Herbaceous Forms

The common herbaceous or subshrubby *Datura* in Florida gardens belong to the Indian species *D. metel* as originally described by Linnaeus. They are low plants, rarely more than 3 feet high, usually grown as annuals although often evergreen and persistent over several years. The flowers, 6 to 7 inches long, are usually white, or may be purple without and whitish within; yellow and reddish forms are met with occasionally.[2] The flowers are never erect, usually horizontal or nodding. Linnaeus gave the purple form the specific name *D. fastuosa,* but there was no excuse for this as the specific characters are identical with those of his *D. metel.* Bailey's illustration of *D. fastuosa* is correct for the species, despite errors in the descriptions; *D. fastuosa* is shown in

big type as an accepted ornamental, but *D. metel* is listed in fine print as a weed!

Because the Indian *D. metel* somewhat resembles the American *D. stramonium,* commonly called thorn apple or Jimson weed, many persons have confused them. *D. stramonium* may grow in cow pastures in Florida, but it certainly is not in cultivation in anybody's garden, because it has a vile odor, and the rank foliage imparts an unpleasant smell to the human skin. Strangely enough, no reference books make any mention of this fact. *D. tatula* is the name commonly given to the purple-flowered form of *D. stramonium.* Its stems and top foliage are usually intensely purple also, and it retains the unpleasant odor of the species.

Here are the chief differences between these two species:

Datura stramonium

Plant usually 2 feet high.
Leaves angled or cut-toothed with an offensive odor.
Flowers erect, smelly; corolla 4 to 5 inches long.
Fruit erect, stays that way in drying, splits open 4 ways when ripe. Fruit oval.
Fruit covered with needle-sharp spines, hazardous to touch when dry. (Smooth-fruited form is called *D. inermis*).

Datura metel

Plant 3 to 5 feet high.
Leaves entire or weakly lobed, with no appreciable odor.
Flowers horizontal or droopy, musty or odorless; corolla 6-7 inches long.
Fruit rounded, hanging down, sometimes splits open irregularly.
Fruit covered with bumps that terminate in short, broad, blunt spines, never dangerous. (Smooth-fruited form called *D. dubia*).

Datura meteloides A. DC. in Dunal[3] is a handsome, herbaceous perennial to 3 feet or more, common along roadsides from Texas to California. It is often cultivated in gardens from Maine to Florida and westward, for the heavily, fragrant, floppy, funnel-shaped white flowers that are sometimes tinged rose or violet. The epithet *meteloides* is misleading; it means "like *metel*" but

---

[2] The red-flowered horticultural form listed by Bailey from South Africa, is not known to Dr. H. B. Rycroft, director of the National Botanic Gardens, Kirstenbosch.

[3] *Datura wrightii* Regel is the correct name for the plant now known as *D. meteloides* of southwestern United States and northern Mexico. *D. meteloides* must be sunk as a name. (Ed.)

203. DATURA CANDIDA

202. DATURA CORNIGERA

actually it is most unlike Linnaeus's *D. metel*. The trouble is that Dunal, who proposed the name, had reference to the Mexican plant *D. inoxia* which he had misnamed *D. metel*. Safford says the corolla of *D. inoxia* has 10 teeth, and that the corolla of *D. meteloides* (which is very similar) has 5 teeth. Bailey's Manual (7) confuses the ordinary gardener by the statement that *D. meteloides* has "5 or 10" teeth. Actually the corolla of *D. meteloides* has 5 teeth and measures 6 or sometimes 8 inches long and 5 inches across; it is always recurved backward on the margin, never forward like a trumpet as in *D. metel*.

Bean's statement that the flowers are "much like those of *D. metel*" refers, of course, not to Linnaeus's plant, but to *D. inoxia*, thereby seeking to perpetuate the error in nomenclature.

The 2-inch, nodding, succulent fruits are prickly; Bailey's Manual says these "burst irregularly." Safford says they do not burst.

The leaves of *D. meteloides* show extreme variations from the textbook *dicta*. Bailey, in Bailey's Manual, and Bean, describe them parrot-like in almost identical words, up to 2¼ inches long, unequally ovate, slightly sinuate—apparently all quoting the same uninformed authority; at least that description was not written by a person who knew the plants. The author has examined plants in California and found leaves up to 6 inches long, often heavily incised and sharp pointed, like a black oak leaf. (See photograph.) The author has examined plants in Missouri, South Carolina, and Florida and found leaves averaging 2½ inches or more, with terminal leaves 4½-5 inches long.

These many flat contradictions on matters of fact are not difficult to understand. *D. inoxia* and *D. meteloides* do look much alike in the laboratory, and a taxonomist, working from the dried remains of plants might easily mistake a poor specimen of one plant for the other. The horticulturist knows the plants in the field: *D. inoxia* is a hairy thing; *D. meteloides* is an attractive plant, with a pretty sheen to its foliage, and lots of heavily fragrant flowers. Similarly with other species of *Datura*, the man who grows the plants knows

how the flowers sit on each kind—vertically, horizontally, nodding, or drooping—and he identifies the plants by these characteristics which his colleague in the laboratory never sees. The garden worker sees how seed pods hang down or stand up, he uses smell and taste to register identities, he knows which flowers change color on the plant after they open. All these identifying features, extremely important in *Datura*, are a closed book to the laboratory worker.

Tree-like Datura with White Flowers

Seven different white-flowered *Datura* trees were described by Safford; it is likely that four of these are cultivated in Florida gardens. Most of them are loosely called "*Datura arborea*" or "tree Datura," but actually the true *Datura arborea* that Linnaeus described is relatively rare. Bailey says most of the plants cultivated under the name *D. arborea* are "presumably *D. suaveolens*." DeWolf said all the specimens bearing the name *D. arborea* which he had seen, actually were *D. candida* or *D. suaveolens*. This makes the going rough for the average gardener who needs a key to tell the species apart.

KEY TO THE TREE DATURAS
GROWING IN FLORIDA

Calyx with 5 short teeth; anthers conglomerate or sticking together _____
_____ *D. sauveolens*
Calyx a spathe without a hornlike point. Lobes of the corolla-limb separated by a gap _____ *D. arborea*
Lobes of the corolla-limb not separated by a gap _____ *D. candida*
Calyx spathelike with a hornlike point nearly as long as the corolla _____
_____ *D. cornigera*

The descriptions of *D. arborea* in both Bailey and Chittenden are highly confusing because historically three different plants were described under this name.

Bean in Chittenden says his *D. arborea* is synonymous with *Brugmansia arborea* that was originally described from Ecuador by Lagerheim (1895) and is now known as *D. affinis* Safford.

241

204. DATURA CANDIDA

205. DATURA SUAVEOLENS

DeWolf says the flowers differ from those of *D. arborea* L. in their glabrous peduncle, their 2- to 5-toothed calyx, and in the margin of the corolla limb which is not heart-shaped between the teeth, but entire or rounded, as in *D. candida*. This eliminates Chittenden because that author's white-flowered form of tree *Datura* does not grow in Florida.

The plant described by Linnaeus, presumably from Peru (1753), is quite different from the foregoing; it is also different from the *D. arborea* described from Peru by Ruiz & Pavon (1799), and now correctly known as *D. candida* (Pers.) Safford, based on *Brugmansia candida* Persoon (1805). Ruiz & Pavon themselves were so confused that they drew a picture of *D. candida* and labelled it *D. arborea!*

Bailey starts out by identifying his *D. arborea* with Linnaeus but fails to mention the features distinguishing that plant from other species called "arborea." Those features are detailed here along lines worked out by Safford and DeWolf:

Datura arborea	*Datura candida*	*Datura suaveolens*
Corolla less than 17 cm. long.	Corolla 20 cm. or more long.	Corolla up to 30 cm. long.
Lobes of the corolla limb separated by a distinct sinus or gap.	Lobes of corolla limb not separated by a distinct sinus or gap.	
Calyx spathe-like, deciduous with the corolla.	Calyx spathe-like, persistent around the mature fruit.	Calyx a short, much-inflated tube with 5 short teeth, 1 to 2 cm. long.
Fruit ovoid (peach-shaped).	Fruit cylindrical.	Fruit a 2-celled, spindle-shaped pericarp which when dry is brown, thin, fragile, glabrous, longitudinally veined with delicate raised nerves, 12 cm. long $\times$ 2.5 cm. in diameter in middle, tapering to both ends, devoid of all vestige of calyx borne on peduncle 7 cm. long
Margin of corolla limb between lobes notched.	Margin of corolla limb between lobes entire or rounded, but not notched.	
Peduncle pubecent.	Peduncle pubescent.	Peduncle 1½ inches long, smooth, glabrous, terete.
Leaves entire, glabrous.		Leaves ovate-oblong, 6-12 inches long, entire often unequal at base.
Anthers distinct.	Anthers distinct.	Anthers conglomerate
Flowers pendulous, with musk-like odor.	Flowers pendulous.	Flowers nodding or drooping, fragrant.

Datura suaveolens is perhaps the easiest of the white-flowered tree species to identify because of the toothed calyx and conglomerate anthers, but confusion attaches to it also in some reference books. Macmillan (8) speaks of the "round, green, prickly fruits" of *D. sauveolens*, oblivious of the fact that they are never round, when ripe they are not green, and they are never prickly.

Many different kinds of *Datura*, both shrubs and trees, occasionally develop double or triple corollas, one inside of another, but this obvious peculiarity is no help at all in distinguishing one species from another. Doubled corollas, usually called hose-in-hose,[4] occur also in *Primula*, *Nicotiana*, and *Rhododendron* (subgenus Anthodendron).

---

[4] M. K. Kay, lexicographer with G. & C. Merriam Co., Springfield, Mass., writes: "The term hose-in-hose undoubtedly stems from an old meaning of *hose*, a sheathe enclosing an inflorescence,' that is now disused except in dialect English. It is very easy to see how several centuries ago, before floral morphology was well understood, such a doubly (or triply) corollate flower could be vizualized as a doubly (or triply) ensheathed. i.e. sheathe in sheathe or *hose-in-hose*, inflorescnece."

207. D. MOLLIS X D. VERSICOLOR (?)

206. DATURA MOLLIS (Florida Peach)

Tree Daturas with Colored Flowers

Safford used the flower color to separate the tree *Datura* species he described; on one side were the white-flowered, on the other the species with colored flowers. Whether this was adequate procedure is now called into question.

Trouble has developed over a pink-flowered tree from Ecuador which Safford called *Datura mollis*—"mollis" means soft-hairy. This is not in cultivation in Florida, but two other kinds of *Datura* with colored flowers (not pink!) have been erroneously assigned by reputable authorities to this species and have been masquerading under this name. More detailed consideration by the same authorities has raised grave doubts in their own minds and has suggested the possibility that these "unknowns" may be merely colored forms of white-flowered species, thereby upsetting a basic separation method devised by Safford.

First of these and one of the most spectacular of all *Datura* plants, is a tree-let to 10 feet or more, widely cultivated in Florida, with very large, hanging trumpet-shaped flowers, usually a foot long and flaring 6 inches wide at the mouth. These flowers open white or light pink but shortly turn a deep, rich peach color that is very striking. As long ago as 1956 this plant was identified as *"Datura mollis"*—which it may not be at all—and it still travels under that name. The following table presents detailed points on which this "Florida Peach" fails to agree with Safford's description of *D. mollis*:

Datura mollis
(after Safford)

Peduncle "clothed with soft hairs."
Calyx spathe-like, 19-20 cm. long, obtusely pointed at the apex, somewhat inflated.
Calyx "densely clothed . . . with soft, spreading hairs."
Corolla light pink, 25-26 cm long, not much longer than calyx. Safford does nit record any change of color.
Corolla: "Nerves of the corolla and margins of corolla teeth clothed with soft hairs."
Corolla limb "bearing on its margin 5 caudate teeth 6 or 7 cm. long, at length recurved."
Leaves pubescent, ovate-lanceolate, entire or remotely toothed, 22 × 10.5 cm.

[5] Suggested as possibly *D. versicolor*, a species of Ecuador. (Ed.)

Florida Peach[5]
(from specimens)

Peduncle 6½-8 cm. long, not hairy. Another specimen clothed in fine hair (seen with hand lens).
Calyx 12.5-15 cm. long, abruptly acuminate, somewhat inflated.
Not so. Another specimen bearing a few scattered hairs.
Corolla opens white or light pink, then turns peach-colored. 25-27 cm. long (twice as long as the calyx, or more).
Not so, or only slightly. Another specimen finely pubescent on nerves.
Caudate teeth 3.5 cm long, recurved.
Leaves beneath hairy, dull, entire, with only suggestion of occasional tooth: oblong acuminate 17-20 × 7-8.5 cm.; one leaf blade 1-1.5 cm. longer on midrib at base than the other.

Enough differences are involved here to challenge identification of the Florida Peach with Safford's *D. mollis*. Admittedly there has been no critical study of *Datura* in general, and flower color alone could not be definitive. Several botanists have reviewed the problem recently and at least two of them have concluded that Safford's description is not satisfactory and that his *D. mollis* may not be a good species. So much variation has already been observed in the Florida Peach that even when a specimen seems to conform to many points in Safford's description, doubts as to identity still persist and suggest the necessity of examining a considerable number of additional specimens before any conclusions can be reached.

Again, the question has been raised by two scholars whether the Florida Peach might not be a color form of *D. candida* (with which it agrees in many ways) or a hybrid. The Florida Peach does not set seed naturally in Florida; no one has tried raising it from self-fertilized seed to see whether there is any variability in the progeny, or whether it is sterile. Consequently the plant must continue to be known as the Florida Peach until its true identity is determined.

The other *"Datura mollis"* which may not be that species at all, developed at Longwood Gardens, Kennett Square, Pa., and was pictured and described by Huttleston (6). The 12-inch leaves are elliptic to ovate, the pendent 12-inch corolla is RHS Nasturtium orange 610/2, fading to buff-white at the throat. Longwood Gardens distributed cuttings to institutions and nurseries, including some in Florida, so that the plant is

245

209. DATURA WRIGHTII (Syn. D. Meteloides)

208. DATURA SANGUINEA

undoubtedly in cultivation in this State.

Unlike the Florida Peach, the flowers on this plant do not open white, then change color; they open orange or apricot and stay that way. The corolla is 11-12 inches long, an inch shorter than on Safford's *D. mollis* and the calyx is 4.5-5 inches long, or 3 inches shorter than on Safford's plant. Expressed another way, the corolla is more than twice as long as the calyx, whereas on Safford's plant the calyx and corolla are almost the same length.

Dr. Huttleston now (1965) is first to admit that his plant differs from Safford's *D. mollis* not only in the color of the flower, but also in that the calyx is long-acuminate instead of obtuse, and that there are distinct notches between the corolla lobes. He is convinced that his plant is of hybrid origin involving *D. mollis* and *D. versicolor* (Lagerh.) Safford, another very beautiful and fragrant South American species whose 10-inch pendent flowers come out white then turn brick red. This perhaps just makes the confusion worse.

Tree Daturas with Red Flowers

The high Andes in South America provide two tree-type *Datura* with red or reddish flowers that are easily set apart from other species because the blossoms are tubular rather than trumpet-shaped. Both of these species survive at high elevations where frost falls every night, yet they have apparently proved too tender for cultivation in California where they have been tried repeatedly. Whether either or both species are now growing in Florida gardens is uncertain, although the United States Department of Agriculture has introduced both of them twice and distributed plants to experimenters.

One was *D. sanguinea* Ruiz & Pavon, which was established here in the 1930's as P.I. 108294 and P.I. 126903. Dr. David Fairchild was in Colombia in November 1941 and as he travelled through the Andes at 5000 feet between Bogota and Villavincencio, he was struck by "the magnificent sight" of the *D. sanguinea* trees along the highway with their hanging 10-inch flowers which he described as "brilliant orange-red with yellow nerves," and "strangely enough, not fragrant." He stopped to pick some of the fruits which are top-shaped, 3.5 inches long, with a smooth skin (no bumps or prickles.) Dr. Fairchild brought the seed back to Florida, and gave some to this author and some to the Fairchild Tropical Garden. Plants from this Fairchild introduction were distributed all over Florida, and some of them may survive today.

The Department of Agriculture also introduced a tree with similar flowers, *Datura rosei* Safford, in 1935 as P.I. 112300 and also ten years earlier as P.I. 58362. (The specific epithet *rosei* refers not to the color of the flowers but commemorates a distinguished botanist J. N. Rose.)

Both of these plants are tree-like shrubs to 12 feet or more with big, pendent flowers that are usually red or reddish, although *D. rosei* flowers have been reported by various authorities as orange and as saffron yellow. The two trees however are easily distinguished by other features outlined by DeWolf:

Datura sanguinea

Leaves entire or sinuate-margined.
Corolla 10 inches long, glabrous.
Calyx with 2 or more large lobes.
Longitudinal nerves in corolla yellow.

Datura rosei

Leaves angular-toothed.
Corolla 6-8 inches long, pubescent.
Calyx spathe-like with a single lobe.
Longitudinal nerves in corolla green.

Conclusion [6]

The foregoing discussion of *Datura* has involved only half a dozen species that are cultivated in Florida gardens, but it illustrates the jumble of contradictions that plagues the genus. Confusion is not confined to these few examples

---

[6] The 1956 Supplement to Chittenden's Dictionary (5) virtually wipes out the 2-column original description of the genus *Datura* and substitutes two columns of new material consisting of a key to the species with additional notes and citations by W. T. Stearn. The key is based on Safford (1) and Danert (9). It corrects many previous errors but raises new questions. The key ignores Safford's *D. affinis* although the original description included this species under the name *D. arborea* (= *Brugmansia arborea*). The *D. arborea* listed in the new outline is a different plant. The key also ignores Safford's *D. hirsuta* which is a point at issue in the present paper. The Supplement's description of the genus admits "about 25 species" (Safford defined 24) but the key accomodates only 14 of these. Thus the material in Chittenden's Supplement only reorganizes the confusion.

but runs all through the 20 or more described species. Of course the flowers of some are exceedingly similar to those of other species, and when this happens the plants have to be separated by their calyces, fruits, leaves, or other characters. Many botanists have been fooled by the similarities and have, as a consequence, given the same name to different plants. Again some species are highly variable within themselves, so much so that even the great Linnaeus and a lot of lesser scholars have been tricked into considering them distinct species.

This situation will not improve until all of the various cultivated forms are grown together in one garden for comparison, and someone (perhaps the same grower) undertakes to do some breeding work to see what happens when the whites are crossed with the reds and oranges. Until actual experiments prove what the plants are, anybody's guesses on nomenclature are just that—guesses!

Apparently all, or at least many, of the tree *Datura* in the Andes are more or less cultivated by the natives, perhaps for their flowers or, more likely, for their narcotic or supposed medicinal properties. Because the plants are easily propagated vegetatively, probably a rather small number of clones is involved, each one selected for some particular property. If each of these clones were regarded as a "species," the confusion would be confounded, for every chance seedling would be different and would have to be recognized. If however, some idea of the natural limits of variation of a sexually reproducing group of these plants could be obtained by growing them experimentally, then taxonomists would be in a position to determine which names are valid, and which mere synonyms.

If this paper could have the effect of provoking such a study, ornamental horticulture would be enriched.

ACKNOWLEDGEMENTS

The author gratefully acknowledges assistance given in the preparation of this paper by Mrs. Julia F. Morton, Morton Collectanea, University of Miami; Dr. Robert W. Read of Fairchild Tropical Garden; Dr. Harold E. Moore, Jr., John Ingram, Dr. Wm. J. Dress, and Robert B. Clark of Bailey Hortorium, Ithaca, N.Y.; Dr. Gordon P. DeWolf of Georgia Southern College, Statesboro, Ga.; Dr. Donald G. Huttleston of Longwood Gardens, Kennett Square, Pa.; Phil Clark of New York Botanical Garden; and Dr. H. B. Rycroft, Director of National Botanic Gardens of South Africa, Kirstenbosch.

Literature Cited

1. Safford, Wm. E. 1921. Synopsis of the Genus *Datura. Journ. Wash. Acad. Sc.* 11:8 pp. 173-189. April 19.
2. Avery, Satina & Rietsema, Albert F. Blakeslee. 1959. *The Genus Datura.* Ronald Press, New York.
3. DeWolf, Gordon P. 1959. Notes on Cultivated Solanaceae (2) *Datura. Baileya* 4:12-23 pp.
4. Bailey, L. H. 1939. Standard Cyclopedia of Horticulture. Macmillan, New York.
5. Chittenden, F. J. 1951. The Royal Horticultural Society D'ctionary of Gard ning. endon Press, Oxford.
6. Huttleston, D. G. 1958. *National Horticultural Society Dictionary of Gardening.* Clar-
7. Bailey, L. H. 1949. Manual of Cultivated Plants. Macmillan Co., New York.
8. Macmillan, H. F. 1948. Tropical Planting and Gardening. Mcmillan & Co., Ltd., London.
9. Danert, S. 1954. *Die Pharmacie* 9:349-362.

Barklya—The Gold Blossom Tree

Both Florida and California have drawn heavily on the flora of Australia for the ornamental trees that have been introduced to brighten residential plantings of the warmer areas of both states. Yet one of the loveliest of them all is still conspicuously absent. This is the Lilac Barklya, *Barklya syringifolia,* which C. T. White of the Brisbane Botanical Garden enthusiastically termed "one of the handsomest and showiest of our native trees."

This tree was named for Sir Henry Barkly (1815–1898) at one time governor of Victoria, though it is scarcely hardy enough to thrive that far south in Australia, but is found growing naturally only in the coastal districts of Queensland to Rockingham and as far south as the Richmond River in New South Wales.

In its native land Barklya is commonly called the "goldblossom tree" in recognition of the large dense trusses of small, bright yellow-orange flowers. These contrast magnificently with the rich dark evergreen foliage. Audas in *Native Trees of Australia* calls "very beautiful" the six- to seven-inch sprays of small, golden, pea-shaped blossoms that come in clusters at the ends of the branches and above the foliage. Herbert in *Gardening in Warm Climates* writes the "brilliant display of small crowded orange flowers" comes in summer (January) and if it follows the same habit in the northern hemisphere, it would provide a much-needed winter-blooming tree on the Florida landscape.

Barklya botanically is a monotypic genus—there is only one species and it is allied to our so-called Orchid tree *Bauhinia.* It makes a tall tree, sometimes to sixty feet, but at first is apparently reluctant to grow. It requires shelter and a moist, rich loamy or leafsoil. "Our most ornamental tree and though a bit slow, worth waiting for," writes Dr. George H. Hewitt of Bellingen, New South Wales. "Most ornamental and well worth cultivating," says Anderson in his *Trees of New South Wales.*

The specific name *syringifolia* was given to this plant because the alternate two- to four-inch, heart-shaped leaves much resemble those of our northern garden lilacs, the generic name of *Syringa.*

Fortunately there is no commercial use for the timber of the Barklya tree and its ornamental beauty never needs to be sacrificed to the sawmill. It is strictly an outstanding ornamental that deserves to be widely planted in suitable areas in the United States. It is propagated by seeds and by cuttings from stems or roots.

211. STENOLOBIUM STANS

210. BARKLYA SYRINGIFOLIA

STENOLOBIUM—The Yellow Elder

The Yellow Elder (*Stenolobium stans* Seem.; *Tecoma stans* (L.) *H. B. K.*; *Tecoma mollis* H. B. K.; *Tecoma stans velutina* DC.) is the glory of southern gardens in autumn. It is a large upright shrub or small tree which must be kept in the background because of its size. A glimpse of its brilliant color from the street is so enticing that one finds oneself invading yards and alleys in order to stand near this tree and enjoying the dazzling beauty of its golden blossoms.

The end of every branch has a large panicle with as many as 60 open flowers at one time. The buds at the ends of the panicles continue to open as the old flowers drop, extending the blossoming season over a period of four or five weeks. The yellow flowers are bell-shaped with a two-inch tube, five rounded and reflexed lobes as well as orange stripes running down the throat. The flowers are fragrant and attract humming birds and bees. The leaves are compound with five to seven narrow sharp-pointed serrate leaflets three inches in length and yellow-green in color.

This small tree, which has a spread and a height of 20 feet has narrow seed pods which are six to eight inches long. When these pods are cut off before maturing it will bloom intermittently throughout the year.

Propagation is accomplished by seed. The plants begin to bloom when about a year old.

When used as cut flowers the stems should be split or crushed and put into deep water in a cool, dark place for three or four hours before being arranged in a vase. They have a luminous quality that makes these sprays seem like liquid gold in the house.

Bailey's *Manual of Cultivated Plants* lists S. *alatum* Sprague from Peru with yellow and red flowers, but the author has never seen this plant in Florida.

Stenolobium is sometimes confused with *Tecoma castanifolia* (q.v.) which does grow in Florida. Both plants have the same "yellow bells" but *Tecoma* leaves are simple, while *Stenolobium* leaves are 3-, 5-, or 7-foliate.

Florida Will Be Only As Beautiful As You and I Make It

The beauty of the landscape might be defined as a visual loveliness that excites and exhilarates the senses pleasurably or exalts the mind or spirit. It is not necessarily confined to color, though often augmented or brought out by contrasts of light and dark, or emphasized by colorful patterning, or effected by lighting displays. Contour of a mountain may be beautiful, or the depth of a yawning chasm may awaken a deep and almost overwhelming awe of the magnificence spread before the eye.

But the beauty of our landscape in Florida as you and I know it, depends solely on how and where brilliant colors are utilized to brighten, decorate or emphasize the eye's acceptance of surroundings that are perpetually green.

Untold numbers of lakes, waterways, sounds, estuaries, and nearly a thousand miles of ocean beaches create unexcelled natural beauty of their kind, especially when accentuated with light and shadow with the help of sun and moon, and can even achieve a wild sort of beauty with the aid of tempestuous winds. Sunrise and sunset provide the only color overtones in these natural surroundings, usually fleeting, often magnificent. But by and large the natural landscape in Florida is an eternal, unending, unchanging vastness of green with nothing but daylight to bring its values to the eye. For without the eye, how can there be any physical beauty? There is a spiritual beauty known to all of us, but that develops in a world apart from material things and knows neither sunlight nor shadow. The physical landscape requires color to achieve the ultimate in beauty.

Ponce de Leon must have been dreaming when he christened his discovery Florida—the land of flowers. There were no flowers, nothing but a vast expanse of green. It is easy to understand why people reaching California are overwhelmed by "the splendor of poppy fields ablaze in the sun of May." The gorgeous bluebonnets of Texas are an eye-filling sight at their peak. And even in midsummer on the Kansas plains, the sight of the sunflowers, "tawny and gold and brown," is more magnificent than many other wild flower colonies. But in Florida Ponce de Leon found no such display because there was none.

In the south end of the State, where Ponce de Leon never arrived, there are two native trees with beautiful flowers—the Geiger tree (*Cordia sebestena*) with quantities of burnt-orange blossoms among the evergreen leaves, blooming off and on several times a year; and the Lignum Vitae (*Guaiacum officinale*) with the richest skyblue starlike flowers all up and down the branches, a breathtaking sight. The Geiger tree is sparingly cultivated half way up the State, but the Lignum Vitae is too slow growing to be useful as an ornamental and is almost never seen out of its native tropics.

Along the north line of Florida, by the Georgia-Alabama border, two beautiful native flowering trees add sparkle to the landscape—the Southern Magnolia (*Magnolia grandiflora*) and the Fever tree or Maiden's Blushes (*Pinckneya pubens*) with its gorgeous Rhododendron-like flowers, but Ponce de Leon did not see these either. He saw green trees and lots of them.

B. Y. Morrison, genius of the world of azaleas, long head of the U.S.D.A. Bureau of Plant Introduction, and kingpin of the American Horticultural Society for many years with both his pen and his purse, wrote the foreword in this

252

author's book on *Flowering Trees of the World* in which 425 color plates depict some of the most beautiful. Morrison was a dreamer too and he dreamed big. He wrote in part:

"It is true, perhaps, that many of the trees shown will be of no value to many a reader as plants for his garden, and that some may never even find a single place in these United States where they may repeat the miracle of their flowering. Does that matter too much? No, a thousand times no, for a mere examination of the pictures alone will open one's eyes to beauty and urge on one's zeal toward new efforts to know and experience, within the possible realm of one's own garden life, things he had never dreamed of.

"In this day and age, dare one dream? A thousand times yes, for without a dream there is no vision, and without vision the people perish."

Hawaii is the classic example of how beauty on the landscape is born in the hearts of the people who live there. Like Florida, Hawaii has no native flowering trees that are outstandingly beautiful in blossom, except *Clermontia* and a few *Hibiscus,* and these are seldom seen. Yet the world has come to think of Hawaii as the ultimate in floral beauty. Why? Because the beauty which lies in the hearts of the Hawaiian people has found expression by the planting of millions of beautiful flowering trees which, in a fertile volcanic soil, pour out their spectacular flowers in eye-filling displays. The trees that bear them are from other warm countries, not from Hawaii. The gorgeous shower trees (*Cassia* sp.) are native to India. The magnificent *Plumeria* trees (which Floridians insist on calling "Frangipani") are natives of Mexico. One Hawaiian woman has 72 kinds of *Plumeria* trees in her garden; can you imagine such a spectacle? Some of these have blossoms 6 inches across! Flowers of *Plumeria* are particularly useful in making leis because they do not wilt when picked. The Hawaiian people hang bouquets around the necks of visitors and natives, mix moonlight and the music of steel guitars and chorus voices, to convince the guests that here is a flower heaven. We have the same moonlight in Florida; all we need is more beauty in our hearts.

Yes, no doubt about it, Ponce de Leon was dreaming. Four hundred years before our time he caught a glimpse of the magnificent spectacle that Florida would become when flowers of every size and hue from every warm country on earth would come here to make their home and add their beauty and color to an indescribably lovely landscape. He saw the beauty that man could and would create here, and it is this vision of long ago that is gradually taking place on the Florida peninsula. Flowering trees by the millions, flowering shrubs undreamed of except by Ponce de Leon, flowering vines and untold numbers of groundlings with bright blossoms—all these are the details of a Florida that you and I are trying to create. The beauty of the landscape is born of the beauty in our hearts, and our State will be, can be, must be, magnificent—a land of flowers. Each one of us must ask ourselves "What am I doing to make Florida more beautiful?"

EPILOGUE

Remember now, My Friend who art so wise!
The moon doth keep its bright
Side ever forward as it sails the skies
In endless silent journey of the night.
He who planned the stars meant all the while
Our petty earthly troubles we should hide
Behind the golden flashings of a smile—
And heaven only see the darker side.
—Colliers, Aug. 1914

I expect to pass through this world but once; any good thing
therefore that I can do, or any kindness that I can show
to any fellow creature, let me do it now;
Let me not defer or neglect it, for I shall not pass this way again.
—Stephen Grelley
(1777–1855)

PUBLICATIONS IN WHICH CHAPTERS
IN THIS BOOK APPEARED PREVIOUSLY

Collecting Plants from World's Tropics.   Miami Herald Aug. 1954

So You Think You Have Trouble—   Miami Herald Aug. 1954

David Fairchild Lives On!   Stuart, Fla. News Aug. 1954

The Most Beautiful Flowering Trees In the World   Fairchild Trop. Garden Bul. July 1967; Horticulture Nov. 1956

Amherstia—Most Beautiful of All   Stuart News March 1956

Canangium—Flowering Ylangylang Tree   Trop. Living Oct. 1963

Lawsonia—Henna—Its Fragrance & Color Are Ageless Lures   N.Y. Bot. Garden Journal, Jan.–Feb. 1966

Flowering Trees for Colder Areas   Orlando Sentinel Dec. 1963

Confusing Chorisia Trees   Natl. Hort. Mag. Jan 1953 & Proceedings of Fla. State Hort. Soc. Nov. 1952

Beautiful Peltophorum   Fla. Homemaker & Gardener May 1956

Delonix—The Royal Poinciana   N.Y. Bot. Gar. Jrnl. May–June 1951

Dais—A Daphne Relative   Tropical Homemaker & Gardener Feb. 1955

Sex & My Ruprechtia Tree   Amer. Hort. Mag. Summer 1968; Miami Herald Apr. 2, 1961

Triplaris   Bulletin of Fairchild Trop. Gar. Oct. 1948

Tabebuia—Our Best Yard Trees   N.Y. Bot. Gar. Jrnl. June 1949; Proc. of Fla. Hort. Soc. Oct. 1960

Spathodea—African Tulips   Trop. Living July 1959

Yellow African Tulip Tree—   Amer. Hort. Spring 1974

Cochlospermum   Natl. Hort. Mag. Oct. 1950

Brachychiton Trees from Australia Thrive Here   Trop. Homemaker And Gardener Dec. 1956

Melaleucas For Florida   SubTropical Gard. Feb. 1951; Amer. Hort. Mag. Apr. 1961

Millettia—Jewels on a String   Natl. Hort. Mag. Jan. 1956

Cassia—The Golden Shower   N.Y. Bot. Gar. Jrnl. Mar.–Apr. 1952

Gigantic Bombax Splashes Landscape   Trop. Homes & Gardens June 1955

Golden Bells from Ecuador   Baileya June 1964

Jacaranda Without A Name   Baileya Dec. 1964

Balsa—Not the Lightest Wood   Amer. Forests Apr. 1971; Nat. Hort. Mag. July 1957

Robinsonella—Tree With Blue Hibiscuslike Flowers   Floriland Sep. 1953

Plumeria—Tree of Tropical America   N.Y. Bot. Gar. Jrnl.

Ochna—What's That?   Trop. Living Jan. 1959

Stenolobium—Yellow Elder.   Proc. of Fla. State Hort. Soc. Oct. 1960

Erythrina—Let's End the Confusion About the Coral Tree   Fla. Homemaker & Gardener Nov. 1955

Oncoba—The "Chic" of Araby   N.Y. Bot. Gar. Jrnl. Nov. 1948

Wercklea—Costa Rican Mallow   Natl. Hort. Mag. Aug. 1951

Lagerstroemia—Tree Crapemyrtles   Natl. Hort. Mag. April 1951 & The Home Garden, Apr. 1952

Brassaia—The Queensland Umbrella Tree   Amer. Hort. Mag. Summer 1971

Cultivated Eugenias In American Gardens   Natl. Hort. Mag. July, Aug. 1959

Bauhinia The So-Called Orchid Trees   Natl. Hort. Mag. Oct. 1956

Callistemon—The Bottlebrushes Like Wet Feet   Natl. Hort. Mag. Apr. 1955

Geiger Tree (Cordia) & Its Relatives in Fla.   Nat. Hort. Mag. July 1955

Datura Species in Fla. Gardens   Amer. Hort. Mag. Oct. 1966

Florida Will Be Only As Beautiful—   Proc. of Fla. State Hort. Society Miami Bch. Nov. 1973

INDEX

257

258